ENTERPRISE
VERSUS BUREAUCRACY

The Development of Structural Air-Raid
Precautions during the 2nd World War

ENTERPRISE VERSUS BUREAUCRACY

The Development of Structural Air-Raid Precautions during the 2nd World War

by

LORD BAKER

O.B.E., Sc.D., F.R.S., C.Eng.

PERGAMON PRESS

OXFORD · NEW YORK · TORONTO · SYDNEY · PARIS · FRANKFURT

U.K.	Pergamon Press Ltd., Headington Hill Hall, Oxford OX3 0BW, England
U.S.A.	Pergamon Press Inc., Maxwell House, Fairview Park, Elmsford, New York 10523, U.S.A.
CANADA	Pergamon of Canada Ltd., 75 The East Mall, Toronto, Ontario, Canada
AUSTRALIA	Pergamon Press (Aust.) Pty. Ltd., 19a Boundary Street, Rushcutters Bay, N.S.W. 2011, Australia
FRANCE	Pergamon Press SARL, 24 rue des Ecoles, 75240 Paris, Cedex 05, France
FEDERAL REPUBLIC OF GERMANY	Pergamon Press GmbH, 6242 Kronberg-Taunus, Pferdstrasse 1, Federal Republic of Germany

First edition 1978

British Library Cataloguing in Publication Data

Baker, John, *Baron Baker,*
Enterprise versus bureaucracy.
1. Great Britain. Ministry of Home Security.
Design and Development Section   2. Air raid
shelters – Great Britain
I. Title
623 ΄ .38   UA926.5   77-30397

ISBN 0-08-022149-1

Printed in Great Britain by A. Wheaton & Co. Ltd, Exeter

To
my wife

Contents

Preface

Though from 1939 to 1945 air raid shelters were of great interest to most people in Britain and were of importance in maintaining the morale of the civilian population, no complete acccount of their development is available. T. H. O'Brien in his volume of the History of the Second World War, *Civil Defence*, had such an enormous canvas to cover that he could not include technical detail. He is conscious of this for he says of the Research and Experiments Branch of the Ministry of Home Security, where most of the shelter work was done "Its responsibilities then rapidly increased and acquired an importance to which most inadequate attention can be paid in this narrative". This is unfortunate as, apart from the purely historic interest, a novel scientific principle guided the war-time work. Had it been more familiar to British engineers it would, in the immediate post-war years, have increased safety on our roads and have found many other applications in industry. I was too much occupied in applying the principle to structural design generally, as mentioned in Chapter 12, and in carrying out my other University duties to tell the story.

Retirement has now given me the necessary leisure. I set out to write an account of the steps taken in design, simple enough for the layman to appreciate something of the thrill and satisfaction of an engineer's work. As the story unfolded another theme was uncovered. This was the struggle that the technical man, armed with new knowledge, almost inevitably has with authority, saddled with many responsibilities such as drafting and applying regulations or making a profit. This is a struggle which may well increase in step with the rate of technological change. The account of it may, therefore, be even more important than the straightforward design story.

I hope that, because it reveals a struggle, no reader will feel that this is a complaining book. In its modest way I consider it to be a success story. It not only tells the layman what engineering is about but shows the young engineer that some of his brightest ideas will meet opposition. He must persist. If he is working on sound principles his efforts should be crowned with success and he will find the struggle exhilarating.

It must not be thought that because this is a war-story it has no relevance today. I have found that innovation in peace-time meets even greater difficulties. Everyone mentioned in this narrative was carrying out the duties of his office, as he saw them, meticulously, with devotion and one aim—to win the War. Any differences we had were over methods. In peace-time, aims are often not so clear cut. It would be gratifying to feel that managers or directors of manufacturing firms who read this book might be moved to re-examine their attitude to their designers and would-be innovators, on whom the future prosperity of their firms almost certainly rests. They might ask themselves whether it is really necessary to put so many difficulties in their way.

I wish to thank the Home Office staff for their kindness. All the day-to-day records I hoped to find in the Ministry of Home Security files seemed to have been destroyed but the

Home Office gave me access to the reports of bomb damage which had been prepared in my Section; also, by a happy coincidence, at the time I was in touch with them all my papers on the Factory (PAD) Committee, which I had forgotten ever existed, came into their hands and were passed on to me. This has made it possible to complete the whole war-time episode by including an account of the Protection of Industry, Chapters 9–11.

I also wish to thank Churchill College, Cambridge. Not only has a place been found in their Archives for my war-time papers but Dr. M. A. Hoskin, then Keeper of the Archives, provided me with wonderful facilities, including the space to set out the mass of drawings and other data in an orderly way, the first step to reducing them to the small compass of this book.

The material taken from official sources is Crown Copyright reproduced with the permission of Her Majesty's Stationery Office. Finally I wish to make it clear that the views expressed are my own and not necessarily those of the Home Office or other official authority.

CHAPTER 1

The Years of Preparation

Britain was first bombed from the air during the 1914–18 War. No attempt was made to provide anything more than emergency shelters then but the attacks were sharp enough to be remembered and as early as May 1924 an Air Raid Precautions Committee was set up by the Government. Terence H. O'Brien, in his volume[1] of the History of the Second World War, dealing with Civil Defence, described in great detail the work of this Committee and the other steps taken in the subsequent fifteen years to prepare the country's defences. There is no need to cover all this ground again here but the truest picture of the conditions existing at the beginning of the Second World War and the problems to be faced then can be given by summarising O'Brien's first six chapters.

The possible effect on morale was recognised. The first of the many Committees to examine the problem of future air attack reported that "the moral effect of air-attack is out of all proportion to the material effect which it can achieve". It recognised that the problem of morale, hitherto regarded as relevant only to the fighting forces, would apply in another war to the entire domestic population. The concluding remark of the ARP Committee's First Report in 1925 was "It has been borne in upon us that in the next war it may well be that that nation whose people can endure aerial bombardment the longer and with the greater stoicism, will ultimately prove victorious."

The scale of attack to be expected was considered by the Committee at its second meeting and estimated at about 200 tons of bombs in the first 24 hours, 150 tons in the second 24 hours and 100 tons in each subsequent 24 hours.

After studying the tonnage of bombs dropped in the 1914–18 attacks and the casualties that resulted, it was concluded that 50 casualties (one-third of which would be fatal) per ton was a reasonable estimate.

The Air Staff revised these figures from time to time until in April 1939 the estimate was ". . . at a daily average of 700 tons of bombs (dropped by some 650 German aircraft) as a maximum effort during the first week or fortnight of a war". As an alternative to an attack of this kind over a week or more, the enemy might choose to deliver as much as 3500 tons on London or elsewhere in the first twenty-four hours.

By 1939 there had been further experience of air bombardment in the Spanish Civil War, 1936–39, and it tended to confirm the Air Staff's estimate that each ton of high explosive bombs dropped on a town would cause about 50 casualties. Thus an attempted knock-out blow involving 175 000 casualties in the first twenty-four hours or a more prolonged attack lasting a week or a fortnight, with the appalling figure of 35 000 casualties a day, might be expected.

The first report of the ARP Committee was a remarkably comprehensive document touching on a surprising number of the many varied topics which were eventually to be

[1] O'Brien, T. H., *Civil Defence*, HMSO and Longmans Green & Co., London, 1955.

embraced in the whole activity of Civil Defence—warning systems, lighting regulations, evacuation, protection against poison gas, protection of persons and property, maintenance of vital services, concealment and casualty services. As far as possible attention will be confined in this book to the single problem of shelters and other structural precautions.

O'Brien notes the need felt by the Committee for experimental data, a matter to which he returns again and again. Of the first report he says, "Measures of protection included not only the problem of shelters but the wider subject of protection of public buildings and those of national importance. The Committee were not sanguine about the prospect of modern buildings withstanding direct hits from bombs employed in a future war but they thought that adequate protection should be possible against fragments and near misses. What was immediately required was technical data, which could only be obtained by direct experiment, about the damage caused by bombs of 500 lb and upwards. The War Office had already been asked to begin experiments on this question, and the Air Ministry and Office of Works should be taken into consultation. Once the essential information had been obtained, the Office of Works should be asked to prepare plans for provision of public shelters and the protection of national buildings." In approving this report, the Committee of Imperial Defence asked Departments to give all assistance possible over experiments concerning protection against air bombardment and gas attack.

In the spring of 1929 the Committee was reconstituted as the ARP (Organisation) Committee and provision was made for a Secretariat "with responsibility for seeing that progress did not languish, and that the reactions of the parts of the plan on one another were studied". Some of its difficulties as O'Brien records "were well illustrated by the problem of shelters, responsibility for examining which lay with the Office of Works. . . . In this sphere material resources assumed outsize proportions. The amount of bricks, mortar and concrete needed to build adequate shelters and the cost of providing these would, the Office of Works considered, be far too large to be viewed as practical possibilities. The ARP Committee had no alternative but to accept the experts' negative conclusions while recommending more detailed study and experiment. But the financial aspect appeared a serious impediment not only to any ultimate scheme of construction but to the immediate requirement of conducting essential experiments. It will be recalled that the Committee's first report had emphasised the need for these experiments, which the War Office had been asked to initiate. Both experiences in this field of inquiry and the funds with which to begin experiments were lacking. The Service Departments alone possessed a measure of these essential ingredients of progress. But the interests of each of these in the effects of air bombardment differed from those of the other two and still more from those of the Civil Department and machinery to co-ordinate experiment and research seems to have been almost lacking. Stalemate over shelters early in 1929 was further aggravated by a clear, and apparently irreconcilable conflict between the need to send the public underground for protection against high explosive and the need to keep them above ground for protection against gas. Practical experiment in defence against gas could in addition be conducted more cheaply and unobtrusively than experiment into the destructive powers of high explosive missiles."

This last remark is most revealing. It echoes the opinion held by those, to be met later, who had to develop shelter designs at short notice during the war, that the concentration of pre-war effort on the protection of the population against possible attack with poison gas was a shrewd political move since it enabled every member of the community to be issued with a protective device, the gas-mask, at a cost of not much more than two shillings per head. This opinion is not meant to belittle in any way the remarkable achievement of those responsible for designing, producing, storing and distributing at the time of the Munich crisis in September 1938, forty million civilian gas-masks. Moreover it will never be known with certainty how far these precautions deterred the enemy from using poison gas as a weapon, but there is little doubt that they encouraged the marked neglect of structural precautions. This neglect, in the form of lack of data and the need for experiments on the effects of high explosive bombs, continues to be noted in O'Brien's account. He says, when reviewing progress in the period 1929–32, "Regarding the various matters included under prevention of damage, the advance by the end of 1932 was, in general, more halting. A plan for protecting London's docks was being completed in detail. But the larger problems of protecting the public by shelters and protecting public buildings were still complicated by lack of information." Major-General H. L. Pritchard, appointed Air Raids Commandant (Designate) in 1933 asked, in his first Memorandum, for "a full scale test of destructive powers of the 500 lb bomb", but the Committee in making its first estimate of peace-time expenditure in the summer of 1934 expressly excluded construction of shelters on the ground of its prohibitive cost.

In March 1935 the Committee obtained Ministers' approval for the extension of the central machinery in the form of an Air Raid Precautions Department at the Home Office. Wing Commander E. J. Hodsoll, who had been secretary of the Committee since 1929, was appointed to take charge. Major General Pritchard retired and his post was abolished. The first task of the new Department was to issue the "First Circular" on ARP . It was the first comprehensive Government statement regarding Civil Defence. It was an invitation to local authorities, and to private employers to co-operate with the government in creating ARP machinery; and to the public to volunteer for ARP duties in their district. The circular contained a straightforward refusal to provide money towards construction of public bomb-proof shelters. Occupiers of premises were told that effective protection could be provided against blast and bomb-splinters from a near-miss at comparatively small cost, though no technical guidance how to do this was given.

O'Brien sums up the position at this time most neatly when he says "the novelty of ARP and the lack of enthusiasm with which the topic was regarded in most quarters combined to give those who composed the embryonic Department a sense of pioneering. They were a small, and in some respects amateur, crew making for deep waters in a ship of light tonnage." Besides the Assistant Under-Secretary in charge the Department was composed of two Principals, two Inspectors and eight others. During the first two years the only real growth occurred in the number of Inspectors who were engaged less in the control of local initiative and efforts than in stimulating them.

Before the Department's formation the Bombing Test Committee had made plans for three groups of tests into penetrative and other effects of high explosive bombs, and the designs of concrete structures to resist such bombs. In February 1936 the Home Secretary appointed a strong technical Committee under the Chairmanship of Sir Arnold Wilson on Structural Precautions against Air Attack. This was asked to recommend, in the light of the information available on damage caused by the main types of bomb, protective measures to be incorporated in new or existing buildings. It appointed various sub-committees. Though these made some advance, the main Committee found it necessary in November 1937, when the ARP Bill was in preparation, to examine the causes of the slow progress. It concluded there was still a serious lack of data on which to base any recommendations, including information about some of the trials carried out under the Bombing Tests Committee's auspices. It recorded its considered opinion that structural precautions were of such importance that it was highly desirable that the Home Office should have an independent research department.

The Air Raid Precautions Act 1937 imposed on local authorities the duty to take precautions for "the protection of persons and property from injury or damage in the event of hostile attack from the air"; these, of course, included provision of shelters for the protection of the public.

In the early months of 1938 the ARP Department was substantially enlarged and reorganised. In particular a Technical Adviser, Sir Alexander Rouse, formerly Chief Engineer, Central PWD India, and later to be known as Chief Engineer, Ministry of Home Security, was appointed to be responsible for a wide range of matters but especially for structural precautions. In O'Brien's words "Three main elements composed the staff, namely permanent civil servants (both from Home Office divisions and from other departments), former officials of the Indian and Colonial Civil Services and retired members of the Armed Forces." Certainly devoted people but not perhaps, as one can see with hindsight, ideal for the recognition and development of an entirely new branch of engineering. Their devotion is in no doubt. The demands on them continued to increase and in July, Sir John Anderson, the Lord Privy Seal—the Minister responsible for Civil Defence—referred to "conditions of prolonged and severe overwork" in the Department.

In spite of these efforts, when the Munich crisis arose in September 1938 and war seemed imminent there were still no shelters and the authorities were driven to hectic trench digging in public parks and other open spaces. If the crisis had not been averted the men who in their youth, twenty years before, had escaped from four years in the horrible trenches of the First World War would have been driven back to similar uncomfortable and inadequate refuge.

The shock of the Munich crisis altered the country's attitude to the whole question of rearmament and Civil Defence benefited, though less than the other arms. As far as shelters were concerned the Government decided, first, to make the trenches dug in the crisis a permanent feature, issuing a standard design of precast concrete trench lining, and secondly to give more help to local authorities over strengthening existing buildings for use as shelters. The most revolutionary move was the decision to issue free to each poorer household, to be placed in its garden, a steel trench shelter, popularly known as the "Anderson", or where a suitable basement existed, steel props for strengthening the floor above.

Anderson shelters and basement propping were not suitable for every type of dwelling and in May 1939, a design was produced for a small surface shelter of brick and concrete to provide the same accommodation as the "Anderson", that is for a household of four or, at a pinch, six people. Tenements and blocks of flats, particularly where the basements were occupied by tenants, presented a difficulty. This was overcome by providing a surface communal shelter usually with brick walls and reinforced concrete slab roof. Later, in August 1939, local authorities were asked to build similar shelters on the streets large enough to hold 50 persons, as public shelters to provide for those caught in the street or without other forms of shelter. All these devices were supposed to give protection from the effects of a "near miss", that is from the effects of a bomb exploding nearby.

The Government continued to resist successfully the quite heavy pressure, largely political, which persisted throughout 1939, and even into the war years, for the provision of bomb-proof shelters for the population at large. They did not, however, prevent local authorities from adapting the small number of existing tunnels and caves for shelter use. London tube stations were also to be used regularly by shelterers.

In January 1939 a fourth main administrative division of the ARP Department was formed to prepare shelter legislation and deal with general policy over structural precautions. The proposal made by the Structural Precautions Committee in 1937 that the Home Office should have its own research establishment was given effect by the appointment of a Chief Adviser on Research and Experiments, Dr. Reginald Stradling, Director of Building Research in the Department of Scientific and Industrial Research. The Research Branch he began to form, with the help of his old Department, was to take responsibility for all experimental work. It was to provide data to Sir Alexander Rouse, now renamed the Chief Engineering Adviser, who would henceforth concentrate on the application of structural and shelter programmes.

By the middle of 1939 these developments at the centre had produced the essential features of the instrument with which the war was to be fought. The decision had been made to appoint Sir John Anderson immediately war broke out to the double office of Home Secretary and Minister of Home Security. His rapidly expanding ARP Department would be fused into the single instrument of a Ministry of Home Security.

The creation of an independent Home Office Research and Experiments Branch early in 1939 provided the means of overcoming the long standing scarcity of data about the effects of high explosive attack. In May the Lord Privy Seal asked some "prominent scientists", as they were described in the Press, to form a Civil Defence Research Committee to advise this Branch. The new Committee approved a programme of research covering a wide range of problems. They were assured that this work would no longer be hampered by lack of funds. By the outbreak of war three full-scale bombing trials had been made, on a brick basement, an underground reinforced concrete structure, and a brick surface building, as well as a blast and splinter trial. The Anderson shelter was also tested. Full-scale trials were, however, still delayed by difficulty in obtaining the use of suitable sites.

CHAPTER 2

The Phoney-War Period

The Civil Defence Research Committee met for the first time on 12th May, 1939 when Sir John Anderson, the Lord Privy Seal, attended to welcome the members and to give them their brief. The Committee consisted of six University Professors—J. F. Baker, J. D. Bernal, A. J. S. Pippard, R. V. Southwell, G. I. Taylor and W. N. Thomas; the Director of the National Physical Laboratory C. G. Darwin, with the Secretary of the Department of Scientific and Industrial Research E. V. Appleton as Chairman. Dr. Stradling was appointed technical officer to the Committee. They met a few days later for their first serious business session. Serious it was, because the members were told of the Air Council's estimate of the scale of air attack which might be expected and the casualties that would result. The prospect of 35 000 casualties a day, one third of them fatal and possibly all in the Greater London area was almost more than the Committee could contemplate. The discussion covered such topics as the availability of cardboard coffins and the practicability of taking barge loads of corpses for dumping in the North Sea.

The meeting took such a morbid turn that I, J. F. Baker, was determined to enliven the third meeting which was to discuss Shelter Policy. Reaching London, I decided that there was time for a haircut before lunch. The way to the barber's shop in the Store I patronised was through the Pets Department and there I saw a pen of handsome tortoises. I bought one and carried it away in a neat cardboard box. At the afternoon meeting, as soon as the item on shelters was reached I said "Mr. Chairman, should we not approach this problem from first principles and see how Nature deals with it?" Whereupon I lifted the cardboard box from the floor, opened it and placed the tortoise on the table. There was a deathly hush; the Committee was not amused.

No records of the Committee's deliberations that day seem to have survived. They are not important here because, while there is no doubt that the Civil Defence Research Committee did remarkable work in many diverse fields, it had extraordinarily little influence on shelter policy or shelter development. The support of a group of "prominent scientists" may have been invaluable to Stradling in his efforts to introduce scientific method into the deliberations of Government departments—and how necessary that was will be seen as the shelter story unfolds—but such a group, collected as a "Research Committee", is not efficient at innovation. Unfortunately, British industry has been slow to realise this. For close on fifty years when faced with new problems it has established research committees rather than development teams and has then been disappointed and disillusioned when satisfactory solutions have not been produced

Soon after the formation of the Committee its members were invited to become full time Scientific Advisers to the Ministry of Home Security in the event of war. Four of them, Bernal, Pippard, Thomas and I accepted.

Thomas, 54 years of age, was Professor of Engineering at University College, Cardiff.

He was a bachelor, a most gentle, quiet man, an intimate friend and confidant of Stradling's. They shared a billet throughout the War. Pippard, 48, Professor of Civil Engineering at Imperial College, London, was Stradling's brother-in-law. They had been contemporaries as undergraduates and had remained close friends. In spite of this, or perhaps because of it, Pippard never settled down at the Ministry of Home Security. He had had a distinguished career as a pioneer aeronautical engineer in the 1914–18 War so that the somewhat subordinate position of a scientific adviser and the aimlessness that was to be one feature of the "phoney-war" period must have been an anti-climax for him. When, early in 1940, the London colleges which had been evacuated in September 1939 returned to London he left the Ministry and resumed his teaching duties. Bernal, 38, was a great prize for the Ministry of Home Security to have secured. Professor of Physics at Birkbeck College, London he was a scientist of great distinction and wide ranging interests. He was a man with a highly developed social conscience, who had been active politically, being particularly critical of the Government's pre-war plans for civil defence and the refusal to provide bomb-proof shelters. Apparently, when he was a member of a deputation giving tongue to these criticisms, some inspired civil servant had suggested that as he was so knowledgeable he should offer his services to the Ministry and help to put things right. Bernal had accepted the challenge. It was to prove impossible to confine his great energies to civil defence problems alone, wide ranging though they became; nevertheless, he was to make important contributions and was an inspiring colleague. I also was 38 and had been Professor of Civil Engineering at Bristol University since 1933. I had, before that, been employed by the steel industry as Technical Officer to the Steel Structures Research Committee which produced in 1936 a new method for the design of framed buildings. This has been described fully elsewhere.[1] As a result of this work I knew something about the behaviour of steel structures and to this I owed my membership of the Civil Defence Research Committee. The fifth Scientific Adviser, not a member of the Committee, was Eric Bird, an architect and editor of the *Journal of the Royal Institute of British Architects*. He was a great, cheerful, amiable bear of a man. He had fought with distinction in the First World War and when accoutred in trench-coat, steel helmet, gas mask and other impedimenta for fire-fighting in the second, he looked as if he was about to go "over the top". He became an authority on the spread of fires in buildings and methods of fighting them.

On Sunday, 3rd September, these men moved to the Forest Products Research Laboratory in Princes Risborough in Buckinghamshire, which had been chosen to house the Ministry of Home Security under the scheme for evacuating Government Departments from London. In the event, those branches which had for long been part of the Home Office clung to Whitehall so that the only part of Home Security to be housed in Princes Risborough was Research and Experiments. This evacuation scheme had been, until almost the last moment, a closely guarded secret. The scientific advisers, on appointment, had been told that they would receive sealed orders, only to be opened on the declaration of war, instructing them where to report. However, the news had leaked out so that having switched off the wireless after hearing Mr. Chamberlain state in lugubrious tones that Great Britain was at war, and shut behind me the door of our Bristol house, from which my wife and children had moved the day before to a farmhouse in Somerset, I was denied the childish thrill of opening sealed orders. I did not escape the irrational and, considering that

---

[1] Baker, J. F. *The Steel Skeleton* Vol. I, CUP 1954 also First, Second and Final Reports, *Steel Structures Research Committee*, HMSO 1931, 1934 and 1936.

I had been fully conscious throughout the 1914–18 War in which I would have been a combatant had it lasted into 1919, rather shameful sense of excitement at going off to war.

I had absorbed all the Air Council's statistics and forecasts so, as I drove as fast as my old Hillman Minx allowed, apparently the only car going east, meeting an endless stream driving west towards what were the evacuation areas, my eyes scanned the horizon for the first wave of enemy bombers. As they had not appeared I stopped in the Market Place at Cirencester and went into the King's Head for lunch, with, after it, a cigar—an unheard of extravagance but justified by the expectation that this might be the last civilised meal for months—then on to Princes Risborough.

The Forest Products Research Laboratory was at the end of a long drive with a turning circle flanked by a red brick office block at one side and laboratory buildings at the other. There was an ominous quiet; it seemed to me that all my colleagues were already in London in the thick of it learning what they could from the bomb damage.

I drew up in the circle, left the car engine running and dashed into the office. I bumped into a large man, "What is happening in London?" The large man, who was Eric Bird, burst into his usual gust of hearty laughter and said "Nothing."

There was no urgency; I went out and switched off the car engine. It was to be more than nine months before any damage worth examination was to be caused by bombs on British buildings. Frustrating months they were to prove for most of the advisers, uprooted from demanding jobs and planted, without any definite duties, in a brand-new and, as yet, unorganised establishment.

Fortunately none of this was realised in the first few days when bombing was expected hourly and there was still a sense of crisis and urgency. I busied myself with the obvious problem of providing more shelters. We ran immediately into the difficulty that, in the re-armament scramble, Civil Defence had a low priority and virtually no extra material, certainly no material with tensile strength, was available. In my search for it I was driven, if not into the highways and hedges, at least into the woodlands of the Home Counties where I found men who could still weave wattle and others who could build gate hurdles. Armed with examples of their craft I returned to Princes Risborough and actually built a few experimental shelters with walls of earth retained within wattle hurdles and roofs of earth piled on gate hurdles. Though a year or so later these wattle shelters were recommended in a Home Security circular for use on building sites, by the time the prototypes were finished in September 1939 the urgency had gone. There were no signs of air attack and local authorities were making headway with the construction of the more orthodox approved shelters.

What is more, the Research and Experiments Department was taking up its well ordered place in the Ministry. It was responsible, as its name implied, for carrying out such research and experiment as was required and for giving advice on, among other things, structural precautions—but only when such advice was requested. The Chief Engineering Adviser, or Chief Engineer, Sir Alexander Rouse, continued to be responsible for shelter design and for advising on engineering questions arising from the shelter programme. The Chief Scientific Adviser, Dr. Stradling, though the majority of his staff were engineers and architects, apparently never questioned this arrangement nor, in the gentlemanly and well ordered world of the Civil Service, did there seem any reason why it should be questioned. All was right with this world—at least so most people felt. Some of us were not quite easy in our minds; those whose duty it was to advise were conscious of their almost complete ignorance. In those early months telephone calls from outside were dreaded because they so often were from trusting people asking for help no one was equipped to give. One of the earliest was from Trinity College, Cambridge, asking how their Library Range could be protected. It is a stone building, designed by Sir Christopher Wren, with the library on the first floor, the ground floor being an open arcade with rows of stone columns down the east side and centre, with a wall pierced with window and door openings supporting the west side. The advice given was to fill the undercroft with timber falsework, as heavy as possible, and then hope for the best, advice that any engineering Fellow of the College could have given.

The Research Committee continued with its work, as will be described briefly at the beginning of Chapter 8, and succeeded in arranging for some tests to be carried out. One was to determine the effect on a nearby trench shelter of a bomb exploding in the ground. The trench linings which were at this time being inserted in many of the systems dug during the Munich crisis were designed to support the weight, or what can be thought of as the static pressure, of the surrounding earth, a load on the roof of 400 lb/sq. ft. and on the sides a thrust varying from 100 lb/sq. ft. at the top to 250 lb/sq. ft. at the base. The tests showed that a buried bomb produced pressures quite different from an explosion in the air. They were of comparatively long duration and there was a permanent movement of the earth. Not surprisingly this produced excessive pressures on a buried shelter. One of the early attempts to reduce damage, which the Committee took seriously enough to test at some length, was to provide an air-gap between the side of the shelter and the face of the trench. This was effective in that the earth, moved irresistibly by the explosion, could flow into the gap. However this was what can be described without unkindness as a typical "Research Committee" solution. It was unpractical, being so expensive as to be ruled out from the start. The face of the trench had to be supported by a retaining wall so the solution meant, in effect, building a shelter within a shelter.

There were from time to time moments of excitement. In January 1940, a German sea mine was washed ashore and exploded outside a hotel at Sandsend on the Yorkshire coast. It did a surprising amount of damage which the Research and Experiments Department decided should be investigated. Eric Bird, with another architect Basil Ward who had recently joined the staff, were despatched. Their beautifully produced thirty page report was of great interest and importance, throwing as it did the first light on the full effects on buildings of blast from a large charge. It is not too fanciful to feel that this report, or some other based on this same incident, alerted the enemy to the effectiveness of the mine against land targets and led to their devastating use, months later, when they began to be dropped by parachute on our cities.

There were trips to give advice which were pleasant and possibly useful. An early one I made with an engineering colleague, D. C. Burn, an old Carthusian, was to Charterhouse School to examine, and to approve since they were excellent, the measures the school authorities had taken to protect the boys. For one educated under more spartan and monastic conditions, as I had been, the visit was memorable for one incident, when the Captain of the House and another boy came into the headmaster's drawing room, just as if they were at home, to escort Mrs. Birley and the Matron into lunch in Hall.

To look ahead somewhat, these trips became much more satisfying and exciting once the bombs began to fall and the advice given could be based on experience. Among the more entertaining was that in June 1940 when Ward and I visited the London Zoological Gardens, on which the night before a number of small 50 kg bombs had fallen. We were to advise Dr. Julian Huxley, the Secretary, on the steps to be taken, not so much to protect the inmates but the residents of the Regents Park district from the animals and reptiles that might escape into the streets as a result of bombing. The animals causing the greatest anxiety were the polar bears, apparently the most savage beasts in the Gardens. The welcome advice was given that no additional precautions need be taken since a bomb which blew open a cage or enclosure would kill the animal in it. Later experience showed that this would certainly have been the case for a caged animal but it is doubtful whether the polar bears on their terrace would have been similarly disposed of. The visit was memorable for Dr. Huxley's discourse on the animals as they were inspected. He was particularly eloquent about the gorillas and was surprised that his visitors knew nothing of their ritual dance. He tried to encourage the animals to perform, but they steadfastly refused so Huxley, without embarrassment, enacted the dance they should have given. Unfortunately, we Home Security officers did not carry ciné-cameras as part of our equipment. The visit ended with an excellent lunch in the Terrace Restaurant where the party sat with a remarkable view of dog-fights between British and German planes, wheeling in the summer sky, this being the height of the Battle of Britain.

The climax of these visits came on Boxing Day, 26th December, 1940, when I had the privilege of inspecting the three bedrooms used by the Royal Family at Windsor Castle, so that we could advise on any steps that ought to be taken to make them less vulnerable. Apparently the King had refused to occupy anything in the nature of a bomb-proof shelter but had agreed to sleep on the ground floor of one of the Castle towers. The walls were very thick, nothing short of a direct hit would have breached them, but the protection against a near-miss was by no means perfect. A number of recommendations were made, including one never made elsewhere. That was that the inside of the walls, which were rough stone, should be covered with fine weld-mesh fabric, that is a very strong wire netting, to prevent the production of missiles by scabbing due to the knock-on effect from an explosion outside. The rooms were furnished with extreme simplicity but the Queen had a number of framed photographs and mirrors in hers. In my letter of 6th January 1941 to Sir Ulrick Alexander, Keeper of the Privy Purse, I wrote tactfully "There were pieces of furniture—mirrors, screens—and pictures on the walls which might be a danger as the result of blast from a 'near miss' ".

Each scientific adviser took his own steps to find useful employment during the unexpected lull from September 1939 until the enemy bombing started in earnest in June 1940. I turned my attention to factory protection.

The Ministries which were responsible for the manufacture of munitions, the Ministry of Supply, the Ministry of Aircraft Production and the Admiralty each had its own independent passive air defence (PAD) department, responsible for providing shelters for the workers and such other protective measures as might be thought necessary. I cannot remember whether we thought that these departments, being analogous to the Chief Engineer's Department in the Ministry of Home Security, should be served by the Research and Experiments Department or whether we were approached for help. It is almost certain to have been the latter. Furthermore, the appeal probably came from Sir Ernest Simon, whose nephews and other members of his firm, Simon Carves Ltd., were working part-time for the Ministry of Aircraft Production, PAD Department (or MAPARP as it was called) in the North-west of England. This took me into aircraft factories in Lancashire and Cheshire. There I stumbled on a problem that I recognised as of first importance. We found that new factories were being built with large spans to enable bomber aircraft, already of considerable size, to be fabricated. However no thought in design had been given to the possibility that these new factories themselves might be bombed. This was clear because, beautiful structures though they were, they were susceptible to what we called "spreading collapse". This meant that there were key parts of the structure which, if cut by even a small bomb, would lead to the collapse of adjacent parts which in their turn would pull down more, and on and on until acres of the factory building and all the aircraft it contained would be destroyed. We later discovered that several types of more orthodox, more common, structures suffered from the same weakness.

Fortunately I had an answer to the trouble. For three years before the War, after the work for the Steel Structures Research Committee was completed, I had, at Bristol, been investigating with the assistance of J. W. Roderick how steel structures behaved when carried beyond the working range and so overloaded that they collapsed. Having in this way learnt something about the collapse condition at that time not usually contemplated by structural engineers I was in a good position to take steps to guard against it.

I succeeded in impressing the Head of the Department, Dr. Stradling, with the seriousness of spreading collapse and the need to combat it. Stradling agreed that his Department had a duty to cover research and development over the whole field of defence against bombing. He was not averse to widening his influence, though as an experienced civil servant he was well aware of the difficulties of working across Ministry boundaries. However he backed me to the extent of providing the resources to set up in the Research and Experiments Department a Design and Development Section.

All labour was, of course, directed by this time in the War so it was not easy to collect staff but there were still pockets of trained men that could be tapped. Practically all architectural work had stopped, so that with Bird's help we had no difficulty in recruiting a team of brilliant young architects including Basil Ward's partner, Colin Lucas, from the firm of Connel Ward and Lucas which had so influenced the British Modern Movement in Architecture, John Madge, later to desert architecture to become a distinguished sociologist, and Leo Desyllas, a founder partner of Architect Co-partnership and who, like Madge, was to die too young. There were some middle-aged men too, including Hugh Hughes of Cambridge who had recently completed a new building for his College, Peterhouse, in that town. Several engineers were found, including D. C. Burn and F. H. Pavry from the Cement and Concrete Association, while a little later, I wound up my consulting engineer's practice in Bristol and brought to Princes Risborough my junior partner E. Leader-Williams.

The existence of my consulting practice is interesting evidence of the liberal attitude in some British universities in pre-war days. When I accepted the Chair of Civil Engineering at Bristol University in 1933 it was understood that my work as Technical Officer to the Steel Structures Research Committee should continue. The University put at our disposal a large office where my research and design staff of six engineers was housed until the work was completed in 1936. The staff then left, but the enquiries and difficulties which the steel constructional industry had for nearly eight years been in the habit of sending me did not stop; I was overwhelmed. This was explained one day to the Vice Chancellor, Dr. Thomas Loveday, who immediately came up with the bright idea that a partner should be found so that I could reply to any enquiry, saying that while I would very much like to deal with it free of charge, as had been possible in the days of the Committee, now I had taken a partner it would be unfair to him not to charge a fee.

On the strength of this official encouragement I went ahead and found the ideal partner in Leader-Williams who had been one of my first assistants on the Steel Structures Research Committee work. He had been unfortunate enough to contract poliomyelitis which had left him seriously crippled. However, with great courage he had completed his training as a structural engineer and was very ready to throw in his lot once again with me. The partnership was responsible for some interesting structures including the extension to the Bristol University Library in which Vierendeel trusses were used and the pioneering, for P. E. Tyhurst at Burnt House Farm, of portal frame farm buildings, though they were not then designed by the plastic method. However, what became our main lucrative work, which had to come to an end when Leader-Williams moved to Princes Risborough, was the strengthening of basement shelters in many of Bristol's largest buildings according to the existing Ministry of Home Security Regulations.

The work of factory protection for which this Home Security staff had been recruited did not come to fruition until 1941 and so will not be described until a later chapter. What was of the greatest good fortune and importance was that this outstandingly able team had been brought together in time to analyse the vast amount of bomb damage that was about to become available, confirming some of the prognostications about factory buildings but throwing a new and startling light on many other problems. Equally important, but not so fortuitous, were the plans which had been laid as far back as June 1939 to make the collection of bomb damage data possible. The Cement and Concrete Association, the research and publicity arm of the cement industry, had approached the Lord Privy Seal and offered to make available to the Government, free of cost, the resources of the Association in the event of war. These included a network of professional engineers covering the whole country who, with very little additional specialist training, made a highly skilled field staff of technical intelligence officers. It was their boast that no incident, from which the staff at Princes Risborough could learn a lesson, went unreported, wherever it might occur. The authorities may have been slow to carry out experiments in the pre-war days but they made amends by their foresight in accepting this offer and setting up an organisation which was to report so accurately most of the full scale experiments the enemy so lavishly provided from 1940 until the end of the war. It was an early and most successful example of operational research.

CHAPTER 3

When the Bombs Fell

In October and November 1939 there were small air-raids on naval targets in the Firth of Forth, Orkney and Shetland. The first British civilian to become an air-raid casualty was at Bridge of Wraith, Orkney, on 17th March, 1940.

The first bombs investigated by the Research and Experiments Department were dropped on Scunthorpe in May 1940 where damage was reported at a steelworks. Bernal and I rushed off to survey the incident. To our disappointment as investigators the damage to the buildings had not been serious and what there was had already been repaired. However, several other bombs had been dropped, one in open ground near a row of railings with, further off, a corrugated iron shed. This proved to be a simple but important incident perhaps because it was the first to be examined in the field. Bernal gave a most impressive exhibition of a natural scientist in action. He went and stood at the centre of the shallow bomb crater; he wrapped his arms about himself and was clearly a bomb, thinking what he would do. The explosive in him would burn, turning into gas which would expand the steel casing until it burst and shot fragments off with great velocity—and there were some of the bars of the railing almost cut through by these fragments, but the bars were unbent by the blast. However, the shed further away had been blown down by the blast, though the sheeting was unmarked by fragments. The Civil Defence Research Committee had been planning tests and considering the effects of bombs for more than six months but it was from that moment of thought by Bernal with the basic evidence before him, that a complete picture began to emerge. Though for many months it was common for reports from the field to remark about the "vagaries of blast damage" when faced with evidence of a street with unbroken windows nearer a bomb and shattered ones further away, in fact the fundamental mathematical laws were soon developed by E. N. Fox, the first Secretary of the Civil Defence Research Committee, so that blast damage could be foretold with great certainty. It was no longer possible, unfortunately, to give any credence to those early war stories which owed more to wishful thinking than to observation. One such, with a wide circulation, described the effect of a bomb exploding in a restaurant, supposedly a Lyon's Corner House. A waitress had just come through the door from the kitchen balancing on her hand a large tray stacked with crockery. After the explosion she stood there unhurt but without a stitch of clothing, still balancing the tray with the crockery on it undamaged.

After our examination of the steelworks we found a public-house in Scunthorpe where we could get a meal and beds for the night. We had no sooner gone to our rooms than the air-raid alert, a loud wailing siren, sounded. The conscientious landlord, obeying the instructions recently circulated, came banging at the bedroom doors ordering everyone down to the basement shelter. Bernal suggested that we should display, probably for the first time, our impressive Ministry of Home Security passes and claim that we were not bound by these petty rules but I being naturally more law-abiding and probably a little

13

frightened, took the line that as officers of the Ministry we should set an example, so down we went. Sitting there, among a motley crew of other guests and the landlord's family, I regretted our move down to the shelter because above our heads were steel joists supporting the ground floor, with their ends resting on brick piers. We had not at this early date the evidence of bomb damage but I knew enough about structural behaviour to feel that this was not the most stable construction for an air-raid shelter. However, the other shelterers were blissfully ignorant and it was so early in the war that the landlord's wife was able to regale us with boiled sweets and oranges cut up into quarters. These did not cheer Bernal, he was sunk in gloom. He did not fear the collapse of the shelter but something much more horrible; he suddenly said "Do you realise what our fate is going to be? We may spend the rest of our lives in Scunthorpe. No doubt further damage is, at this moment, being done to those vast steelworks. We will have to spend the whole of tomorrow surveying the damage—and so it will go on *ad infinitum*."

However, no damage was done to the steelworks that night but a message came from Home Security saying that bombs had fallen on Peterborough, so away we went.

The only incident of any note was at the town's open air swimming pool which, not surprisingly, as a result had been closed to the public. Flourishing our famous passes, we had no difficulty in getting in. There we found some slight structural damage. It was a beautiful warm sunny day so we decided that a satisfactory view of the damage could only be obtained from the middle of the bath. The somewhat reluctant attendant provided us with bathing costumes and so we were able to combine our inspection with a refreshing bathe.

I was fortunate enough to be involved in the first all night raid on a city, an unexpected development which was to have serious repercussions on shelter development. I had offered to go back to Bristol for a few days in June to help with the University degree examinations. I took my wife and two small daughters, who by this time had joined me in the safety of Princes Risborough, to stay with our friends the Tyhursts. They occupied a tall Georgian house in Somerset Street on the ridge overlooking the medieval city. We had only been in the house a couple of hours and were about to go to bed when there was a loud explosion apparently at the bottom of the hill. A minute or two later the alert sounded. Bill Tyhurst, who was Divisional ARP Warden of the Central Division, which in the years to come was to suffer a greater intensity of bombing than any comparable area in the country, rushed out to his post. The Tyhursts had a shelter-room deep in the basement of their house. To this the household made its way, to the great delight of the children. The shelter was equipped with every imaginable comfort except a telephone extension, so I climbed the stairs, lay on the floor in the hall by the telephone and had a running commentary of the raid from the Central Division whenever a lull allowed the Divisional Warden to report.

Early next morning I made contact with the Home Security technical intelligence officer for the region, whose duty it was to report the damage. Together we set out to view it. The raid was not, by later standards, a heavy one but the damage was much more than anyone had really visualised in spite of the Air Council's pre-war estimates of casualties. It was widespread too so that it was difficult to know where to make a start. One thing was immediately obvious, the damage was much more than one officer could report before the evidence was removed by the demolition squads. At Bristol, fortunate conditions existed because I could call for volunteers from the staff of the University Engineering Department. These willingly put aside examination papers and did a fine job of reporting many incidents.

It has to be admitted that, if one could forget the casualties and the upset caused to those whose property suffered structural damage, surveying and reporting was a fascinating exercise. In those early days almost every incident revealed some new unexpected facet and the survey was more like detective work than straight engineering. There was plenty of excitement and a slightly hysterical sense of entertainment. For the first time unexploded bombs appeared; the area around Temple Meads railway station was peppered with them. Sappers, a platoon of soldiers of the Royal Engineers, had been moved in and the public moved out. When we Ministry of Home Security officials appeared we were welcomed by the soldiers. We owed our popularity to the fact that some other branch of the Ministry had recently issued a pamphlet about defusing unexploded bombs, so we two hapless officials, who had no knowledge of the art, were greeted as experts and were soon following the pamphlets' instructions unscrewing the fuse covers and shorting the condensers by grasping the terminals with a pair of pliers. Fortunately the bombs remained unmoved.

Some of them yielded valuable data, particularly about penetration. A large bomb had gone through the concrete road of the station approach and many feet into the clay beneath where it could be seen at the bottom of the deep hole. I was quite excited at this and said, "Marvellous, this really will tell us something about penetration. Drop the end of your tape down." The Regional officer, instead of dangling the free end of his measuring tape down the hole until it reached the bottom and then reading off the depth of penetration, in his excitement threw down the hole the other end, the heavy leather covered case, which landed with a resounding "klonk" on the bomb. He then had to haul in hand over hand one hundred feet of tape, which took what seemed an interminable time. It was a good thing those bombs really were duds.

Back at Princes Risborough the first step was to organise support for the regional technical intelligence officers throughout the country by recruiting volunteers from university staffs, as had been done at Bristol, and from other professional organisations. These men generously gave their services throughout the war; without their help it would have been impossible to collect so much invaluable detailed damage data which made it possible not only to improve our defence against air attack but later to plan our aerial offensive.

The reports soon began to reach Princes Risborough in ever increasing numbers as the German Air Force turned from its attempt, in the Battle of Britain, to destroy our fighter force to its efforts to hit our war production and cow the civilian population. Particularly from 7th September, 1940, the first great day raid on London which continued into the night and was followed by almost nightly raids for three months, the technical staff in the Design and Development Section was hard pressed analysing the damage. They had some surprises. The most serious related to shelters.

Trench shelters which had appealed so much to local authorities were highly vulnerable. Some of the most widespread and serious damage occurred in trenches which were lined with the standard pre-cast concrete units, consisting of wall slabs standing in slots on a floor unit with a similar roof unit resting on the top of the walls as shown in Fig. 3.1. If carefully installed they provided stable support against the passive pressure of the earth but when disturbed by the effects of an explosion they were inherently unstable. If the roof slab was lifted only a couple of inches by a remote explosion then the side slabs would be forced inwards by the static earth pressure and the roof slab would then fall. Similarly if the wall slabs were pushed in on one side by a near miss, the roof slab would be unsupported at one edge and would fall.

The unsatisfactory behaviour of these and other kinds of standard shelters can best be appreciated from a study of a few typical incidents. One occurred at Southwark on 21st October, 1940 when a small high explosive bomb of 50 kilogramme weight (50 kg HE) dropped ten feet away from the side of a 50 person trench shelter, 30 feet long, lined with pre-cast concrete units. The crater formed was 20 feet diameter 4 feet deep. The damage report states "Shelter demolished. Roof lifted which allowed sides to cave in. Roof then collapsed. Side nearest explosion moved 3 feet towards other side wall. Floor broken up along centre." The total number of occupants was not stated but 24 people were killed.

Large trench shelters were shockingly vulnerable to a direct hit owing to the funnelling effect on the blast. On 16th October, 1940 a 250 kg HE bomb had made a direct hit at the junction of two galleries of a 3000 person underground public trench shelter, lined with pre-cast concrete units, in Kennington Park, London. As will be seen from the portion of the damage Report reproduced in Fig. 3.1, the shelter was wrecked over an area of almost 10 000 square feet and 46 people were killed.

Certain other forms of trench lining were also unsatisfactory for much the same reasons. One at Norwich consisted of reinforced concrete portal frames at intervals down the trench supporting a pre-cast concrete slab roof and pre-cast concrete slab sides. A high explosive bomb, reported to be 50 kg but possibly larger, exploded 32 feet from the side of the trench making a crater 15 feet diameter and 6 feet deep in loam. The portal frames buckled allowing the slabs in roof and sides to fall into the trench where five people were killed.

At Middlesbrough a 250 kg bomb fell between two 50 person semi-sunk communal shelters, 10 feet from Number 1 and 15 feet from Number 2, the crater being 16 feet diameter and 6 feet deep. The lining of these shelters was made of semi circular cast iron sections 12 feet diameter, 20 inches wide and $\frac{7}{8}$ inch thick. In each shelter five of the cast iron sections were demolished and of the 36 occupants of Number 1, five were killed.

The only standard shelter which behaved well was the Anderson, the arch shaped trench-lining of heavy corrugated steel sheet. The occupants often survived the nearest of "near misses", that is to say when the shelter was on the lip of the crater formed by the bomb explosion.

Semi-sunk brick shelters with reinforced concrete slab roofs were common but unsatisfactory. At Southwark on 29th December, 1940 a 250 kg HE bomb fell two feet from the entrance to two 50 person public shelters built in April 1940. Both shelters were demolished except for short lengths at the far ends. Of the 18 occupants, 14 were killed and three were severely injured. However, in other incidents, there were some remarkable escapes. An extensive system of semi-sunk brick and reinforced concrete slab roof shelters had been built in the grounds of a school, covering an area of 7000 square feet. A 50 kg HE bomb penetrated the roof and exploded inside causing the havoc shown in Fig. 3.2 with walls demolished and roof collapsed. Fortunately, there were only 38 occupants at the time of the incident and only one was seriously injured, an adult pinned under fallen brick work. Three children nearby were released unhurt.

Though some basement shelters were excellent, notably those in multi-storey steel framed buildings which were as near bomb proof as anything available to the public, others, including those strengthened by means of the standard issue of tubular steel struts, were not satisfactory.

A basement shelter for 85 people, under a three storey house in Kings Road, Chelsea, was subjected to a near miss on 11th September, 1940, a bomb exploding 10 feet away blowing in the front wall of the house up to first floor level. The basement was streng-

CROSS SECTION
BEFORE DAMAGE

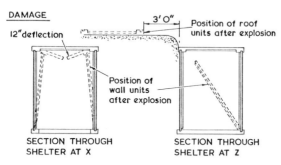

DAMAGE

12" deflection

3' 0"

Position of roof
units after explosion

Position of
wall units
after explosion

SECTION THROUGH
SHELTER AT X

SECTION THROUGH
SHELTER AT Z

DETAILS OF SHELTER

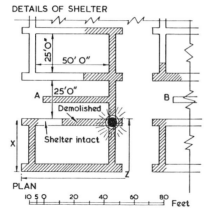

25' 0"

50' 0"

25' 0"

A

Demolished

B

Shelter intact

X

PLAN

10 5 0   20   40   60   80
Feet

Fig. 3.1

thened by three rows of four standard tubular steel struts supporting a 4 inch by 3 inch rolled steel joist above which was a lining of 9 inch by 3 inch timbers instead of the standard corrugated iron sheeting. The two centre struts of the row nearest the bomb were blown away, the steel joist was twisted and allowed the timber sheeting to sag. The remaining struts did not collapse, but successfully supported the considerable debris load; nevertheless four of the 85 shelterers were killed.

There was a shocking incident at Stoke Newington on 13th October, 1940 when a bomb, probably 250 kg, made a direct hit on a five storey tenement building, exploding at ground floor level. The building above was demolished. There was a public shelter for 300 persons in the basement. It had been strengthened by introducing below the basement ceiling a layer of 6 inch by 4 inch by 4 feet long pre-cast concrete deck units supported by 13 inch by 5 inch rolled steel joists of I-section at 4 feet centres, their ends resting on brick

Fig. 3.2

walls. The explosion demolished the brick walls which let down the steel joists and in their turn the concrete units. Almost all these, when salvaged, were more or less undamaged showing that their collapse was not caused by the falling debris from the building above. Their collapse did, however, allow the debris to fall on the shelterers, 157 of whom were killed.

Two nights later there was another disaster at Lady Owen's School, Finsbury. A bomb exploded 5 feet outside the basement wall forming a crater in the road 35 feet in diameter. The building was shaken down and so was the basement strengthening which consisted of steel joists supported at their ends on new $13\frac{1}{2}$ inch thick brick walls and on 9 inch by 9 inch timber struts. Eighty shelterers were killed and 20, seriously injured, were dug out of the debris.

A somewhat similar shelter in Suffolk Street, South Norwood, survived a near miss on 18th October, 1940 but only because the strengthening steel joists were continuous over three supports. Two similarly stengthened shelters where continuity of the steel joists was not provided were in the Treasury Building, Whitehall, and a house in Croydon. Both were subjected to direct hits, the first on 18th October and the second on 5th December, 1940. The walls collapsed or the joists were forced off their seating plates causing fatal casualties.

One almost comic incident occurred in the Town Hall at Reading. A semi-basement passage, 10 feet wide with a segmental arch roof about 100 feet long had been strengthened by supporting the arch at every 4 feet 3 inch with a bearer elegantly shaped to the arch, standing on a stout 6 inch by 6 inch square central vertical post. A baffle wall three feet high of 18 inch hollow concrete blocks had been built outside the window at the end of the passage. This wall was not reinforced with steel rods as it should have been by 10th February, 1942 when the incident occurred. A 500 kg bomb fell on the pavement outside the building 9 feet from the wall and dead on the centre-line of the passage. The blast shot the concrete blocks through the window and down the passage where they had a mammoth game of skittles in which the first 17 posts were knocked over leaving only the very end one standing. How far the collapse would have been limited if the strengthening structure had been continuous it is difficult to say but the question is fortunately of academic interest only since no one was in the shelter. The time of the incident was 16.34 hours, maybe the Town Hall tea-break.

The most serious blow to the public's confidence was the behaviour of the surface shelters built in the streets with brick walls and concrete roofs. They did not behave well. Their walls were shaken down by either earth shock or blast and the ruins were there for all to see. Fig. 3.3 shows a typical scene of devastation caused by only a medium sized 250 kg bomb falling in Woodford Place, Paddington, on the night of 7th October, 1940. Three Victorian houses three storeys high were demolished together with a long length of brick surface shelter, the end of which can be seen still standing.

Small shelters were demolished completely by near misses from small bombs as happened to a twelve person shelter in Lambeth with $13\frac{1}{2}$ inch walls of brick laid in sand lime mortar and a 5 inch thick reinforced concrete slab roof. The 50 kg bomb fell 6 feet from the end of the shelter making a crater 9 feet in diameter and 2 feet deep. The walls of the shelter were demolished completely while the roof slab was lifted, moved several feet and fell on the ruins of the walls. Fortunately the shelter was unoccupied. A similar bomb falling at Sutton, Surrey, in almost exactly the same position relative to a 30 person communal shelter divided into three compartments, demolished the end wall. The rest of the shelter was severely damaged but the walls held up the roof mainly because of its length and continuity over the two internal division walls. Only three of the 13 shelterers were slightly injured. The shelterers in a similar incident at Birkenhead on 2nd October 1940 were not so fortunate. The 50 kg bomb fell 4 feet from the wall of a four compartment communal shelter, with $13\frac{1}{2}$ inch brick walls and 5 inch thick reinforced concrete roof, producing a crater 10 feet in diameter. The wall of one compartment was demolished and of the 10 shelterers in it, two were killed, two were seriously injured and two lightly injured.

The effect of larger bombs was similar. At Manchester on 7th October, 1940, a 250 kg bomb fell 35 feet from a 24 person public shelter built of $13\frac{1}{2}$ inch brick walls with a roof made of 10 inch wide 2 inch thick pre-cast concrete slabs laid across the walls and covered with *in-situ* concrete. The crater formed was 27 feet in diameter. The earth shock moved the nearest wall outward at the top so that the roof, with the exception of two slabs at one end, collapsed.

A large 500 kg bomb fell at Stepney between two 48 person communal brick surface shelters divided into four compartments, 75 feet from one and 100 feet from the other. The crater was 50 feet in diameter and 8 feet 6 inches deep. Two compartments of the nearer shelter were demolished and one of the farther. At Poplar a parachute mine exploded on a three storey building 170 feet from the end of an exactly similar shelter. The end compartment collapsed.

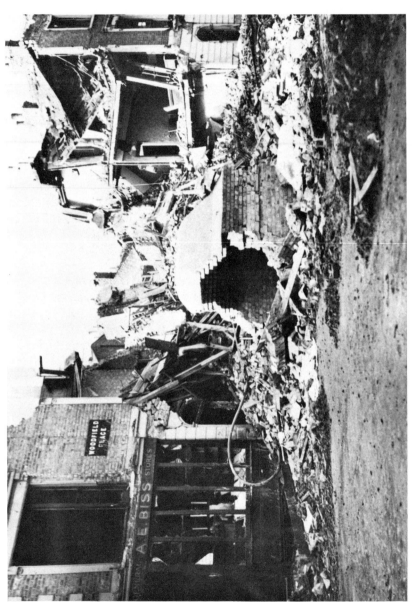

Fig. 3.3

Even before the Research and Experiments Department had analysed the kind of data just described, the unsatisfactory behaviour of many of the standard forms of shelter was realised by the people living in those streets which bore the brunt of the blitz. The awful conditions in London, particularly in the East End which after the daylight raid of 7th September, 1940 was to have no unbroken rest at night for almost two months, began to tell. There was no panic among the people of London but there was shock and some discontent. By the end of the month the position was serious and morale was certainly suffering. This impelled the Prime Minister, Mr. Winston Churchill, to make changes in his team. On 4th October, 1940, Sir John Anderson was appointed Lord President of the Council and Mr. Herbert Morrison, the Labour Party statesman who had throughout his public life been closely identified with London, took over his responsibilities as Home Secretary and Minister of Home Security.

Morrison threw himself with great vigour into his task. Only a few days after assuming his new duties he went out to Princes Risborough to visit the Research and Experiments Department. There, at a meeting with Stradling, Thomas, Bernal and myself, the shelter problem was discussed. The Minister was highly critical of what had been provided. He brought his denunciation to an end with a direct question "Who can design more efficient shelters for us?" To the surprise of myself as much as of my colleagues I replied "I can". Morrison was somewhat taken aback at this immediate response. He turned to Stradling and said "What right has this man to say he can?" Stradling, who had a slight impediment in his speech, noticeable at moments of high excitement, stammered out the somewhat exaggerated remark "He is the greatest authority in the World on the design of steel structures". "Well," said Morrison, "let him go to it", and with that the party adjourned for lunch.

CHAPTER 4

Fundamentals

It is always difficult for a designer or innovator to pinpoint the exact moment when the key to a problem came to his hand or the light dawned on some quite new approach. It is unlikely that I had, at the meeting with Mr. Morrison, a perfectly clear concept of the principles to be applied to obtain efficient shelters, particularly as the problem had not been in the forefront of my mind, since shelter designs were still considered the particular preserve of the Chief Engineer.

However, one thing was already apparent from the evidence of the actual bomb damage. For some reason which it is still impossible to explain adequately, the standard shelters approved by the Ministry to give the people protection from high explosive bombs had not been designed to withstand explosions. Almost the only protection they were capable of giving was from fragments arriving as if shot from a gun or from debris dropping vertically from some undisturbed source. The standard trench linings and semi-sunk shelters collapsed catastrophically when subjected to earth shock or blast. The basement propping which would have effectively supported the debris of the collapsing building was not there to do its job because the impact effect of the explosion, which caused the debris, had already knocked the propping out of place. The brick surface shelters, with walls thick enough to keep out bomb fragments, were blown down by the blast or shaken down by the earth shock and precipitated the roof, which could have given protection from falling crater debris, on to the heads of the shelterers. The only explanation possible will appear far fetched to all but some involved in civil defence before the war. It is that the designers felt that they were not working in a real world, that their products would never be used or put to the test, that they were, in fact, playing a part in some fantasy.

Whatever the explanation, and it is tragically bound up with that lack of experiment which was a recurrent theme of Chapter 1, so ineffective were the pre-1940 shelters that almost any engineer with access to the damage reports could have done better. However, I had a firmer basis for my assertion to the Minister. As mentioned briefly in an earlier chapter, for ten years I had been completely absorbed in an investigation of the behaviour and design of steel framed buildings. Just before the War began it had reached a most fruitful stage, revealing the fundamentals of collapse. When principles of behaviour are thoroughly understood in this way, then a designer, without necessarily seeing all the details, can claim confidently that efficient designs based on these principles are possible. This work must now be outlined.

There should be no need for the layman to feel any misgivings at the short excursion into engineering science that is to follow. Of all branches of engineering, that dealing with structures is the simplest. Children at a tender age become structural engineers when they put a plank across a ditch. Without consciously scorning the refinements of design calculations they soon acquire the "practical" man's sense of what is safe and what is not. Sometimes, of course, it lets them down into the wet ditch much as, to this day, spectacular collapses of large bridges occur at enormous cost in material and often, regrettably, in human life. Nevertheless, in spite of these disasters, due sometimes to the practical man's crass ignorance but in the main to neglect of details, the underlying principles of structural theory are simple enough.

The work I was engaged on for about the first seven years as Technical Officer to the Steel Structures Research Committee was the derivation of an improved method of designing, that is to say finding the necessary sizes of the I-section steel members of, the multi-storey steel framed building, that familiar type much used for tall office blocks, shown diagrammatically in Fig. 4.1. It consisted of lines of vertical columns, continuous from top to bottom of the building, supporting lines of horizontal beams which in their turn supported the floors and walls, external and internal. The bottom and top flanges of the beams were connected to the vertical faces of the stanchions by cleats made of lengths of angle iron, bolted or riveted to both members. To simplify his design calculations the designer was in the habit of making the sweeping assumption that all the joints behaved as frictionless hinges. The steel industry felt that a more efficient structure, that is one using less steel, would result if a design method could be based on the real behaviour which was then unknown, so the SSRC team set to work to find what this was. We had a wonderful time developing new instruments and using them to test a number of London buildings then under construction, including the Cumberland Hotel at Marble Arch and a new railway office block at Euston. These tests showed that the beam to stanchion connections were far from hinges, in fact, they behaved virtually as rigid joints, so the steelwork designer had been living in a world of fantasy not much different from that of the pre-war shelter designer. He had chosen fantasy for the usual reason that the real world was too difficult to contemplate.

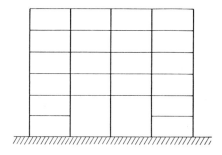

Fig. 4.1

The rigidity of the joints meant that the steel framed building was highly redundant, that is to say it had many more members or constraints than were needed to make it stand up as a structure. In those days, before the emergence of the electronic computer, it was a mammoth task even to analyse the stresses in a known structure of this kind, but to design one, that is to settle the sizes of the members so that they would be strong enough, before knowing anything about the structure, was several degrees of difficulty greater. This synthesis is, however, the essence of engineering, providing much of its charm and challenge and differentiating it from pure science which is essentially analysis.

After some years' work Professor Batho of Birmingham University and I succeeded in producing a rational and, in our opinion, workable design method. There is no need to describe it. It was fully explained in the three Reports to which reference was made in Chapter 2.

What is important here is the fate of the method. It was ignored. Though the steel industry had financed the seven year long investigation its designers found the method too complicated for their taste; they persisted in their fantasy. This disturbed me. I could not believe that the steel framed building had reached its zenith in 1936; there had to be an acceptable way of designing more efficient structures and so, unaided by the steel industry, I continued to look for it.

The SSRC design method, in common with every other since the emergence of a theory of structures a hundred years or more before, was based on the behaviour, or supposed behaviour, of the structure in its working range. The object was the perfectly understandable and defensible one of proportioning the members so that, under the worst arrangement of loads the structure was likely to meet in its working life, no member would be overstrained. It would, in fact, remain elastic; that is to say it would return to its original condition when the loads were removed. This had always been ensured by stipulating a maximum working stress, or force per unit area of the member, much less than the failing stress of the material, which must not be exceeded in any member. It was this necessity to deal with elastic stresses in the highly redundant steel framed building which so complicated the SSRC method. I began to wonder whether a fundamentally different approach might not be more fruitful. From my experience as a designer of structures that had been built, I knew that when I was anxious, for instance, when a gale was lashing the structure, my thoughts did not fly to a particular member and wonder whether the working stress there was being exceeded somewhat. What worried me was, would the whole structure collapse? I thought, therefore, that a rational, and possibly simpler approach would be to consider the state of the structure at total collapse, find a method of proportioning the members to guard against that and then check, by the simpler process of analysis, that under working conditions the structure was elastic.

To find all about collapse I started experimental work, testing in the laboratory small steel beams and portal frames as shown in Fig. 4.8(a). In this I was soon joined by John Roderick, a Bristol graduate later to become a distinguished professor of civil engineering in the University of Sydney, who was supported at a salary of £300 per annum, by the Welding Research Council whose Secretary, A. Ramsay Moon, had become enthusiastic about the work.

Structural mild steel is a remarkable ductile material. If the ends of a straight bar of such steel are pulled apart (Fig. 4.2(a)) the bar stretches, the strain or extension (e) per unit length being proportional to the stress or load (p) per unit area, as shown in Fig. 4.2. If, after stretching as far X, the load is removed, then the bar returns to its original length. It has thus behaved elastically. If load is re-applied the line OX is retraced and, as the load is increased further, continues to point Y. Then, a critical stress, called the yield stress (p_y), having been reached, the bar suddenly extends to P, this plastic and irreversible extension YP being about ten times the elastic strain at Y. The plastic extension extends over the whole length of the bar and should not be confused with the local "necking", which occurs near the centre of length of the bar, preceding fracture indicated by the point F on the stress-strain curve, Fig. 4.2.

Incidentally X in Fig. 4.2 might represent the working stress (p_x) of the elastic design

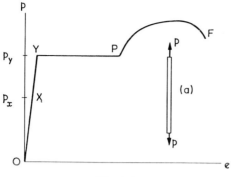

Fig. 4.2

method, well below the yield stress (p_y) which the elastic designer would think of as the failing stress of the material.

The first structure tested at Bristol was a straight beam of uniform section resting on simple supports at its ends and carrying a uniformly distributed transverse load. Under such a load the beam will bend (Fig. 4.3) as the young structural engineer with the plank over the ditch knows, the relation between the applied load **W** and the central deflection δ being as shown in Fig. 4.4. Longitudinal bending stresses are induced in the beam, distributed linearly over the cross-section as in Fig. 4.5(a), the greatest pull or tensile stress being in the bottom face of the beam and the greatest compression stress being in the top, all, of course, having their largest values at the centre of length of the beam where the bending moment is greatest. The beam can be considered, quite rigorously, as a collection of longitudinal bars acting as that of Fig. 4.2; incidentally bars in compression behave basically as do those in tension, except, of course, that under load they reduce in length instead of extending.

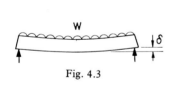

Fig. 4.3

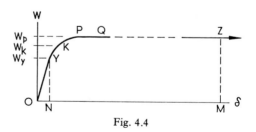

Fig. 4.4

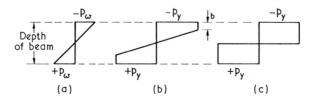

Fig. 4.5

The form of stress distribution shown in Fig. 4.5(a) persists so long as the beam behaves elastically, the central deflection δ being proportioned to W. As W increases so does δ and so does p_w the largest bending stress. This state of affairs continues until, under a certain load W_y, represented by the point Y, Fig. 4.4, the bending stress reaches the critical value p_y, the yield stress of the steel. Under the elastic design method this load W_y would be considered the "failing" load; in fact the beam is relatively unmoved by it.

Further load can be added safely. It will, of course, cause the beam to bend further. This in its turn will stretch the longitudinal fibres more so that they can accommodate the additional bending moment. The stress condition at the centre of length of the beam can be deduced from Fig. 4.2. As the outer fibres stretch further they enter the plastic range YP, Fig. 4.2, still maintaining the yield stress p_y. The distribution of stress in the beam under some load W_k, represented by point K on Fig. 4.4, is shown in Fig. 4.5(b), the fibres for some distance b into the cross-section of the beam having entered the plastic range. The relation between the beam's central deflection and the load it carries will no longer be linear but, as shown at K, Fig. 4.4, the curve will begin to bend over. As even more load is added to the beam it bends further and more fibres reach the yield stress, so that the dimension b, Fig. 4.5(b), increases until at a critical load W_p it reaches the half depth of the beam, Fig. 4.5(c), and the whole of the cross-section at the centre of the beam has become plastic. In fact a "plastic hinge" has been formed at the centre of length of the beam and collapse occurs, the central deflection growing very large as shown in Fig. 4.4. But there is nothing catastrophic about this "collapse", it is a slow and dignified proceeding. It only continues while the full load W_p is doing work on the beam; if this load were reduced minutely after collapse had started then deflection would immediately cease at some point such as Q. The concept of a plastic hinge and the full plastic moment (represented in Fig. 4.5(c)), that must operate to cause it to rotate, rather like a rusty hinge that needs force to turn it, became of the greatest importance in shelter design, as it has since in structural engineering generally.[1] Anyone who has taken a wire paper-clip in his fingers and unbent it, and bent it again, has experience of developing a plastic hinge.

At the danger of labouring the point, it must be emphasised that the behaviour of the ductile beam described above is entirely different from that of a brittle member. Had the beam been of brick or unreinforced concrete with a failing stress of p_y, then its behaviour as load was applied would have been as shown in Fig. 4.4 up to the point Y, when this critical stress would have developed. The beam would then fracture, catastrophically, into two pieces. It would be unable to sustain any load, so that the load deflection curve would be completed by the vertical line YN.

Plastic behaviour is even more interesting when the structure is continuous, and so redundant. Fig. 4.6(a) shows a beam identical with that of Fig. 4.3 except that it is built-in at its ends, so that they cannot rotate when the beam bends under load, thus producing redundant restraints there. While the beam is elastic the greatest bending moment and therefore the greatest stress occurs at these restrained ends. It is at the ends therefore that plasticity first develops and where eventually, under a load $\overline{W}_y$, Fig. 4.7, plastic hinges form. However this beam is far from collapse. It continues to behave virtually as an elastic beam now restrained at its ends by the moments needed to make the plastic hinges turn. As the load is increased further plasticity develops at the centre of length and eventually under a load $\overline{W}_p$ the whole section there becomes plastic and collapse occurs, with large deflection because the beam has become a mechanism by the formation of three plastic

[1] The general application will be found in *The Steel Skeleton*, Vol. II, CUP, 1956.

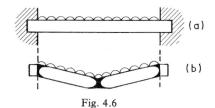

Fig. 4.6

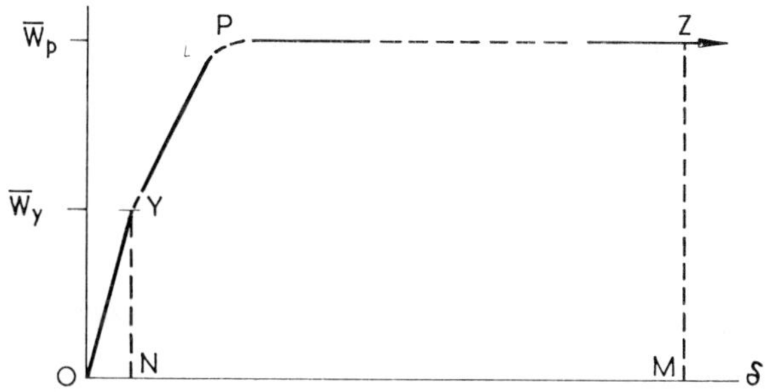

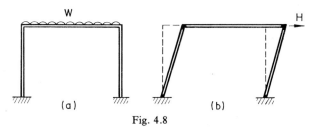

Fig. 4.7

hinges as shown in Fig. 4.6(b). The value of $\overline{W}_p$ (Fig. 4.7) is twice that of the load causing collapse of the same beam with simply supported ends (Fig. 4.4).

The pre-war Bristol tests showed that the beam would behave in exactly the same way and collapse under the same load $\overline{W}_p$ if it were part of a rectangular portal (Fig. 4.8(a)), with legs at least as strong as the beam. Under any more general load system the portal would not collapse until four plastic hinges had been developed. For the special case of the horizontal load, Fig. 4.8(b), the plastic hinges would form at the four corners.

The load-deflection curve, Fig. 4.7, must have been in my mind when I made my rash statement at the meeting. It proved to be the key to the design of efficient shelters and all other protective devices. The key can be defined by the simple principles of *continuity* and *ductility*. *Continuity*, not only to avoid the disastrous knock-on effect that occurs when discrete members are subjected to impact or shock loads, but to obtain that increase in collapse load illustrated by the comparison of Fig. 4.7 with Fig. 4.4. *Ductility*, so that collapse only occurs by the formation of plastic hinges at a high load causing large deflections.

Blast or earth shock from a near-miss subjects a structure to intolerably high forces which cannot fail to produce excessive stresses, but the energy transmitted is not usually intolerable. This energy can be absorbed by a properly designed protective structure

Fig. 4.8

which is only asked to perform once so that large permanent deformation is tolerable. This is quite different from a peacetime structure in which the deflections must be elastic and small, so that the structure regains its original form each time it is unloaded.

The greatest elastic deflection in the beams examined above was ON (Figs. 4.4 and 4.7). The plastic deformation could be many times larger, say OM. The energy absorbed by a structure in deforming is measured by the area under the load-deflection curve. The greatest energy that could be absorbed elastically is therefore measured by the area of the triangel OYN, but the energy absorbed plastically is the vastly bigger area OPZM.

When the energy to be absorbed is known then the protective structure can be designed, using the plastic method, to have a collapse load and a permanent deflection of such magnitudes that the area under the load-deflection curve equals this energy.

CHAPTER 5

Design of Improved Shelters

While the Design and Development Section, known in the Department as RE4, undoubtedly started to "go to it" the minute the Minister of Home Security had left Princes Risborough, there were some administrative ends that had to be tied up if the work was ever to see the light of day. Some wise counsellor had certainly made it clear to Mr. Morrison that the Chief Engineer was considered the sole authority on shelter design and might not welcome initiative from the Research and Experiments Department. This was certainly clear to Stradling who foresaw breakers ahead and wished to avoid them. I recorded in a private note immediately after Morrison's visit that Stradling said to me "You must take this right off my shoulders, just keep me informed. You are to represent me on all Committees and at all meetings including Miss Ellen Wilkinson's Shelter Policy Committee. You can have every facility including any transport you need."

The Minister took the practical step of calling a meeting which incidentally lasted for three days from 15th to 17th October. At it were represented the Chief Engineer's Branch and the Research and Experiments Department. The Minister demanded from it a unanimous report. He may even have put the matter to some intimate in stronger language and threatened to lock the parties in a room until the report was forthcoming as he claimed, quite erroneously, to have done where the indoor-shelter, described in Chapter 6, was concerned. He says in his Autobiography:[1]

"The experts—engineers and scientists—would have argued for weeks. I told them that I intended to lock them up in a room until they agreed, promising to arrange to send food in to them. I reported to Churchill that I had taken this attitude and he was delighted, saying that he would back me to the limit. The experts had their designs agreed upon and completed within twenty-four hours."

Confusion between the two cases would not be surprising after a lapse of twenty years since Morrison says in his Preface "I must admit that I have suffered a little from not having kept a diary over the years. It would have been an aid to memory and a check on fact."

RE4 concentrated first on designs for the surface shelter to be erected in the streets which in its original pre-war version had behaved lamentably and caused much alarm and despondency. My first design was obviously influenced by my immediate pre-war research work. It consisted of steel portal frames fabricated from 7 inch by 4 inch I-sections welded together at their joints and placed 6 feet apart as shown in Fig. 5.1. Unreinforced brick walls were built between the portals and around them; the roof was a 5 inch thick reinforced concrete slab with the upper flanges of the portals buried in the concrete. In the first design a foolish and elementary mistake was made, as will be seen from Fig. 5.1. The shelter was extended for a distance of approximately two feet beyond

[1] Lord Morrison of Lambeth, *Herbert Morrison—an autobiography*, Odhams Press Ltd., 1960.

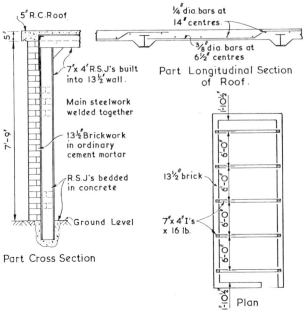

Fig. 5.1

the end portals. This meant that these ends were neither continuous in the proper sense nor ductile. Before this shelter could be built it was realised that however well it might stand up to bombing, it was excessively expensive in steel, 50 lb per person sheltered being needed. This was quite out of the question and so another solution was essential.

One might have thought that the obvious way to economise in steel would be to design a reinforced concrete box structure. Oddly enough there was some doubt about the reliability of reinforced concrete when subjected to explosions. This undoubtedly dated back to the very early days of the war when the only evidence was that from reports of the Sino-Japanese war and also from some later Swiss tests. The Japanese photographs showed damaged warehouses where the reinforcement in the roofs appeared to be stripped of concrete and hung in festoons.

While war-time tests were soon to vindicate the behaviour of reinforced concrete, in October 1940 there was no chance of using it because of the impossibility of obtaining timber or any other satisfactory material for use as formwork into which the wet concrete could be poured. Attention was, therefore, turned to reinforced brickwork. This was by no means a novel material and it is not surprising to find that its use had been contemplated by Major-General Pritchard in pre-war days because it was associated with design against shock, having been much used in the reconstruction of Quetta after the disastrous earthquake of 1935. The exact form of construction used at Quetta was ruled out in October 1940 because it required special skill and such was the urgency under which the designers were working that they could not contemplate demanding anything of the kind.

A very simple solution was found. It was noticed that in a wall built in English bond, the kind of work any bricklayer could produce, there was room for vertical steel reinforcing rods $\frac{1}{4}$ inch diameter to be inserted within the mortar joints. The rods were spaced $4\frac{1}{4}$ inches apart in the thickness of the wall and at pitches of $6\frac{3}{4}$ inches and $11\frac{1}{4}$ inches in the length of the wall, as will be seen from Fig. 5.2, which shows the plan of alternate brick courses. The shelter was intended for use on existing road surfaces and therefore the reinforcing rods were not taken down into the floor or road but the walls were built on a bituminous felt course laid on the road surface. This was a sound method of building construction and it was thought to have the added advantage that it would enable the shelter to slide when subjected to earth movement and so absorb some of the energy. The reinforcing rods ran continuously up through the walls and were carried into the roof as shown in Fig. 5.2, since the whole purpose was, as far as possible in this mixed construction, to provide a ductile portal structure as Chapter 4 had shown to be necessary.

It will be noticed that in the design of these shelters no attempt was made to absorb a definite amount of energy. At this stage in the development of the art no one had any idea what energy a surface shelter might be called upon to absorb as the result of a near miss. The designs therefore were confined to making use of as much ductile material as was available placed most advantageously in structures which obeyed the fundamental principles set out in Chapter 4.

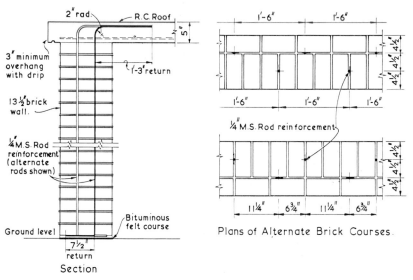

Details of reinforced brick walls for surface shelters

Fig. 5.2

The next urgent problem was to provide strengthening for the existing standard trench linings which, as was indicated in Chapter 3 were structurally unsound. The simplest system was to provide an independent steel framework which would under any condition support the pre-cast concrete roof, floor and side units. This was accomplished by placing rectangular steel frames made of 3 inch by 3 inch by $\frac{1}{4}$ inch angle with rigid joints transversely at 6 foot intervals along the trench, connecting them at their corners by longitudinal members, 5 inch by 4 inch angles at the top and 3 inch by 3 inch by $\frac{1}{4}$ angles at the bottom. A more elaborate but attractive system was to build baffle walls in reinforced brick or reinforced concrete at intervals across the trench, so limiting the effect of blast from a direct hit, and supporting the longitudinal steel members on those walls.

The shortcomings of basement shelters have been made clear in Chapter 3. They arose in the main from the use of brittle members such as brick piers or walls, lack of continuity and a neglect of the effect of lateral loads, resulting in no provision for bracing or other lateral support. It was a straightforward matter, therefore, armed with the new principles to draft recommendations for improved designs and for making good deficiencies in existing shelters. These need not be dealt with in any detail here.

All this work was pushed on with great speed. This is shown by a Minute dated 26th October from me to Dr. Stradling.

"I attended a meeting of the Committee for Shelter Action held at the Home Office on Thursday 24th October. The agenda is attached, very little of which was of interest to this department.

"Under 2(a) Miss Wilkinson asked what steps had been taken over the improvements to surface shelters. I was able to report that I would hand over to the Chief Engineer suggested methods of strengthening existing surface and trench shelters and a new design for brick surface shelters. This has been done and copies of the drawings will be forwarded on Monday.

"This covers Paragraph 5 of the Minutes of the meeting held with the Minister on Sunday 25th October.[2] We are, of course, continuing with the consideration of new designs of surface shelters and tests will be carried out at Stewartby, but we cannot, of course, wait for the results of these before putting out the new designs.

"Under 8 of these Minutes the Chief Engineer has, as described above, received from us one idea for strengthening existing trench shelters and we are energetically dealing with other ideas."

While all the new work was clearly well under way by the end of October it naturally took some time for an official circular to be issued. This appeared as Home Security Circular No. 290/1940 on 11th December 1940, passing on to Local Authorities all the recommendations supposedly arrived at by the Joint Committee. Unfortunately, the Circular was not as complete as it might have been. This is shown by the Minute which follows dated 20th December, 1940 from me to Stradling, who I was, as instructed, keeping well informed.

"Home Security Circular No. 290/1940 dated 11th December, 1940 was received in the Research and Experiments Department on Tuesday 17th December, 1940. This circular aims at putting into effect the improvements in shelter design decided on in principle by the joint meeting 15th to 17th October of the Chief Engineer's Branch and the Research and Experiments Department called by the Minister when he demanded a unanimous report. Subsequent discussions have taken place between the Chief Engineer and representatives of the Research and Experiments Department on points of detail and all the designs used in the Circular were made by the Research and Experiments Department with Mr. Webster's[3] closest collaboration. The circular contains, however, a number of proposals which were not agreed to by the Research and Experiments Department and are regarded by them as technically unsound and omits others which they considered are of vital importance. It must not be considered as representing a unanimous opinion as demanded by the Minister. The Research and Experiments Department was not given any opportunity of studying the document in proof form.

[2] Clearly this date is incorrect, it must have been 13th October.
[3] Webster was the Chief Engineer's deputy.

The first point of difference is in:

(A) *Brick and Concrete Surface Shelters (2) (a) 1 Defective mortar*, where the scraping and grouting with cement mortar of the joints of certain brick shelters built with lime mortar is recommended. This was repeatedly condemned as it is considered to be no solution of the problem. The Research and Experiments Department always stated that the lime mortar shelter was unsafe and could only be made reasonably satisfactory by inserting a strengthening steel portal.

In (B) *Trench shelters (a) Design*—it is stated that "in future designs of this type (pre-cast linings with vertical side members, etc.) should not be used unless strengthened as indicated below". It was agreed with the Chief Engineer that the use of BCF and similar units as linings for trenches should be discontinued.

The most serious differences from the views expressed by the Research and Experiments Department arise in (C) *Basements (c) Strutting*. A full survey of the behaviour of basement shelters was carried out and recommendation was made on 19th November 1940, to the Chief Engineer.

The whole section, (c) *Strutting*, is weak. The first paragraph is obscure and does not lay down any methods of improving design or correcting faulty strengthening. The same can be said of the second paragraph. A comparison of these paragraphs with the Research and Experiments Department's recommendations "Review of the Strengthening of Basement Shelters" dated 15.11.40 will show the discrepancies.

The third paragraph shows a complete lack of appreciation of the dangers to basements. It was laid down in the Research and Experiments Department's recommendations that all brick piers should be replaced by steel struts and that in new shelters brick piers should never be used. The lateral strength of a strutting system is at least as important as the vertical strength and brick piers reinforced or not, are not satisfactory from this point of view. The recommendations in the circular that "light" steel stanchions should be added to brick piers may well be misleading and the steel stanchion must virtually replace the brick pier if it is to be effective.

No mention is made of systems in which the strengthening beams are carried on existing walls and this practice does not appear to be prohibited for future basement shelter.

The experience of raids in London is, in itself, sufficient condemnation of several of the recommendations of the Circular. Thus, out of 24 incidents reported in detail in which more than 20 persons have been killed, eight have occurred in strutted basements and four in trenches lined with pre-cast slabs. Out of a total of 1100 deaths occurring in these incidents, 409 were in basements of the type still allowed to be built under the new regulations.

The worst failures, in particular the Stoke Newington incident, occurred where brick walls were used to support rolled steel joists. Whatever the conditions which strutted basements were originally designed to resist, practice has shown that they are, in fact, predominantly affected by lateral shock from near misses and must now be designed to resist these. Direct hits on the building over the shelter have, when this has been unframed, also often resulted in failure of strutting due to transmitted shock through the walls as in the Treasury basement. It is undesirable to have shelters at all in unframed buildings. If they are there they must be effectively supported and braced if we are to avoid the repetition of such disasters.

174 deaths have occurred in trench disasters, collapse occurring at great distances

from the explosion. There would have been far more had the trenches destroyed been more fully occupied. Many trench systems now in use are death traps and should be closed or, if absolutely needed, braced. There is no case for making new trenches with pre-cast sides. In our opinion the issue of the new Circular will serve to perpetuate many of the worst errors of past shelter construction and, if acted on, will lead to still further disasters and loss of life. In view of this it is imperative that it is followed immediately by another in which is incorporated the agreed principles of reinforcing strengthening worked out by the Research and Experiments Department."

There is no evidence that Stradling took any action as a result of this strong Minute. If he did it was ineffective because the Circular No. 290/1940 remained unchanged.

This sad bickering persisted down the years. While it must have been irritating to the Chief Engineer, who represented Authority, to be told what to do by a mere adviser and one he probably considered a young upstart, my concern is also understandable. When all is said and done the Minister had demanded an agreed recommendation, the Design and Development Section did have the knowledge and felt passionately that if lives were not to be lost unnecessarily the new design information must be used. It is pathetic that the Chief Engineer was not confident enough to make use to the full of the sound advice that was being passed on to him but this conflict between authority and the innovator is not unusual and is likely to become more acute as technological change accelerates, outstripping the knowledge of those in authority.

While the Circular was being drafted, preparations were in hand for the important tests of the new design of brick surface shelter. They were carried out in February 1941 on land put at our disposal by the London Brick Company at Stewartby in Bedfordshire. They simulated very closely the conditions arising from the nearest of "near misses" when a 250 kg bomb exploded after penetrating a road on which the surface shelter had been built.

Six shelters of different designs, with internal dimensions 27 feet 9 inches long, 10 feet wide and 7 feet 9 inches high, were arranged in a circle about the hole in which the bomb was to be buried with its centre of mass 9 feet 6 inches below ground level. The nearest corner of each shelter was 13 feet from the bomb and the furthest 37 feet. The crater was expected to extend under the near corner of each shelter and, in fact, this proved to be so. Shelter No. 1 was the ordinary unreinforced brick surface shelter which had behaved so disappointingly; it had 13½-inch thick brick walls built of English bond and a flat 7½inch thick reinforced concrete roof. Shelter No. 2 was the new design of reinforced brick shelter. It was identical with Shelter No. 1 except for the ¼ inch diameter steel rods running up through the brickwork and carried into the reinforced concrete roof slab. Shelter No. 3 was my first design with welded steel portal frames built into and supporting the reinforced concrete roof with panels of plain brickwork built between the portals. Shelter No. 4 was another reinforced brick shelter, this one built in a modified Flemish or Quetta bond. It was reinforced with ¼ inch mild steel bars in concrete cores at 13½-inch centres. The amount of steel in this design was slightly less than that in Shelter No. 2. Shelter No. 5 was a strengthened lime mortar brickwork shelter. This was to test the suggestion made by me in the Minute to Stradling, of inserting light steel portal frames inside the highly unsatisfactory shelters, which due to an unfortunate Ministry directive had been built in certain parts of the country during an acute cement shortage. Shelter No. 6 was quite unusual and must have been suggested by some extremely influential person whose identity is now forgotten. It was an unreinforced brick shelter, the bricks being built in a vertical bond and keyed into the 7½-inch thick reinforced concrete roof. The idea behind it was to supply increased strength in horizontal shear without the use of steel.

When the bomb went up, the sight was really spectacular. Earth and portions of the slab rose in a plume to a height of about 250 feet and then fell to earth again. The radius of the crater was 18 feet, so that the near corner of each shelter was about five feet inside the crater. Within this radius the road slab was broken up into large pieces, some of which were thrown up vertically while others were flung outwards, either causing damage to shelters or passing overhead and landing at relatively large distances from the crater. One weighing a ton was found 85 feet away and quite sizeable pieces flew 200 feet, the smaller debris reaching 400 feet from the centre of the circle. Miraculously, or so it seemed to the designers, when this debris had settled, there at the centre of things were some shelters, at least, still standing. The spectators rapidly covered the 200 yards, which separated them from the scene of destruction.

Those members of the RE4 design team who were present could not conceal their joy. Both reinforced brick shelters were standing, so was the welded steel portal shelter but to my shame the end two feet had inevitably fallen off, this can be seen in Fig. 5.3. This picture needs some explanation, not so much of what is seen but of what can no longer be seen. On the extreme left is the corner of the English bond reinforced brick shelter, then comes the welded portal shelter which is easily recognised because it is undamaged apart from the shameful fore end. Then to the right is a space, within it, behind the man (marked by an arrow) examining a crack in the next shelter, is the debris of the normal unreinforced brick shelter which collapsed almost completely; then, being examined by the man is the other reinforced brick shelter. In the middle foreground is a reinforced concrete slab. This is not a piece of the original road slab, it is in fact the roof of the vertical bonded unreinforced brick shelter, the walls of which have disappeared entirely. Another shelter, which cannot be seen was the lime mortar strengthened with steel portals, which also collapsed showing that my suggested strengthening was not satisfactory. This was because the principles were not obeyed. The steel portals were ductile but there was no continuity between them and the weak walls.

The actual tests were carried out by personnel from the Road Research Laboratory of the Department of Scientific and Industrial Research. They provided a factual report on the result of the tests but they also allowed themselves the luxury of some comments. In these they said that Shelter No. 3. the welded steel portal frame, undoubtedly offered the greatest protection against explosion. Even under the very severe conditions of test it would seem unlikely that anyone in this shelter, except perhaps persons in the small end bay nearest the bomb, would have been killed. In Shelters Nos. 2 and 4, that is the reinforced brick shelters, there would almost certainly have been some casualties. The normal unreinforced brick shelter was severely damaged and Shelters Nos. 5 and 6 were completely demolished. It is certain that the casualties in these three shelters would have been very heavy.

The reporters' comments were fair enough except that they were almost certainly in error suggesting that there would have been casualties in the reinforced brick shelters. The only damage, as can be seen from Fig.5.3, was severe cracking. This had in the main been caused by the shelters being thrown off the road slab which was of only limited dimensions. The reporters were, of course, not yet versed in the new outlook. No structural collapse in the true sense of the word had occurred in the reinforced brick shelters. Cracks, however severe, would not hurt anyone.

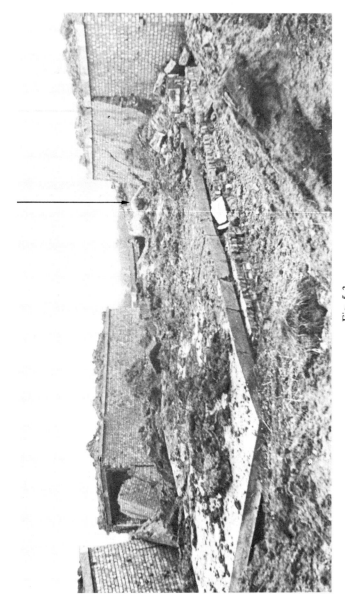

Fig. 5.3

A ciné film of the explosion had been taken and this yielded the most surprising information. It showed that the reinforced brick shelters were thrown up in the air and slewed around to such an extent that they came off the road slab. Measurements showed that the vertical acceleration of the floor near the remote end of a shelter, that is at a distance of 37 feet from the bomb, was about 20 times the acceleration due to gravity. As acceleration falls off rapidly it means that at the end near the bomb the acceleration must have been much greater than 20g. There are times when ignorance is bliss. If these facts had been known to the design team before we began our work it is unlikely that we would have dared to put forward such lightly reinforced continuous structures. It must be remembered that in the English bond shelter the size of the reinforcing rod $\frac{1}{4}$ inch diameter and the spacing was settled entirely by the geometry of the bond and yet, by good fortune, the ductility and continuity provided had been sufficient to produce perfectly satisfactory results.

This shelter known officially as "Brick Surface Shelter reinforced in accordance with Circular 290" was an immediate and immense success in exactly the form in which it left the designer's drawing board. It went straight from the drawing board to the municipal engineers to be built in thousands on our city streets long before the tests had been carried out, such was the urgency as mentioned in my Minute of 26th October to Stradling. In spite of my confidence in the newly propounded principles this took some courage but it was nothing to the energy that went into persuading the Chief Engineer's Branch and the administrative officers of "O" Division at Headquarters to allow it.

By a happy chance the first reports of the behaviour of these shelters in the field, or rather in the city streets, reached us before the Road Research Laboratory report was published in April with its alarming information about the accelerations involved or the pessimistic deductions about possible casualties.

The first recorded incident involving a Circular 290 Reinforced Brick Shelter occurred on the night of 9th April, 1941 at South Shields. A very large 1000 kg bomb fell 38 feet from the end of the shelter which had six occupants. The crater formed was 55 feet in diameter and 13 feet deep in clay. The bottom corner of the shelter nearest the bomb was slightly damaged, probably by flying masonry, and the shelter moved 4 inches on its damp course, but no occupant received any injury. Ten days later a similarly constructed public surface shelter was subjected to an even more severe test in London at West Ham. A parachute mine exploded 74 feet from the end of the shelter. The end wall and the entrance baffle wall of the shelter were demolished but the shelter was otherwise undamaged and it certainly looks as if these two return walls which collapsed were not tied in to the roof. In fact the same elementary error that I had made in Shelter No. 3 of the Stewartby tests had probably been repeated. However, there were no casualties.

An early case, occurring on the night of 4th May, 1941 in Bootle, caused the design staff some amusement and great satisfaction. The Circular 290 Shelter involved was in the form of a 48 person public surface shelter divided into four compartments. It was occupied almost to full capacity. A 50 kg bomb exploded 5 feet from the side of the shelter making a crater 12 feet in diameter and 6 feet deep. That is to say the crater broke right under the shelter and, though the bomb was smaller, the condition created was identical with that of the Stewartby tests. The shelter moved bodily to a maximum of 18 inches as shown in Fig. 5.4 causing the wall next to the explosion to crack vertically in several places. The roof was fractured in three places, over both entrances and the internal division wall. Under the latter fracture the wall on the side away from the crater had been ripped open, the size of

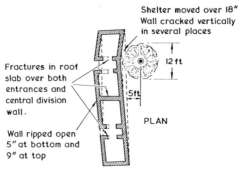

Shelter moved over 18"
Wall cracked vertically
in several places

Fractures in roof
slab over both
entrances and
central division
wall.

12 ft

5ft

PLAN

Wall ripped open
5" at bottom and
9" at top

Fig. 5.4

the gap being 5 inches at the bottom and 9 inches at the top, damage almost indentical with that observed in the Stewartby tests. In spite of this, and what the Road Research Laboratory reporters might think, no occupant was injured, but one was inconvenienced. He was a small boy who was highly indignant because the wall of the shelter had not only moved laterally it had lifted and in coming down again had trapped the welt of his boot so that he had to make his escape from the damaged shelter barefoot. This homely incident impressed us with the fact that the shelters were thrown violently about even more convincingly than did the analysis of the ciné films of the Stewartby tests which were just then becoming available. What was remarkable, of course, was the resistance of the human frame to the enormous accelerations to which the shelterers were subjected.

Immensely successful and economical as were these free-standing reinforced brick shelters built straight off the road slab, the designers immediately turned their attention to producing an improved version which could be built when time and materials became more readily available. This was a complete box section starting with a 6-inch reinforced concrete floor built on top of the road surface with a layer of building paper between. The floor was of reinforced concrete and reinforcing bars were carried up from the floor into the brick wall of the shelter which had to be made with Quetta or Flemish bond so as to provide the necessary tolerance in positioning the wall reinforcement. The remainder of the shelter was identical with the Flemish bond shelter tested at Stewartby. Details of this shelter later appeared with other more advanced designs in a Consolidated Circular published in March 1942.

The principles of continuity and ductility as applied to surface shelter design having been proved up to the hilt, the next task facing RE4 was the development of economical methods of strengthening the many thousands of unsatisfactory unreinforced brick shelters which still survived. However, while that was in hand a mildly embarrassing situation developed. It arose from the initiative of a number of City and Borough Engineers who were responsible to their local authorities for shelter construction. Many of these men had ideas of their own about improvements that could be made and "O" Division at Headquarters was inundated with suggestions. Had it been left to me I would certainly have explained to these professional engineers the principles of continuity and ductility which must be obeyed in design but the fact is that no one but I and my immediate team had any real confidence, at this time, in the principles.

It was decided at Headquarters, therefore, that the most satisfactory, though somewhat expensive and time consuming, method of satisfying everyone, would be to take a selection of the most promising designs or perhaps, since none was promising, it might be more honest to say a selection of those from the more distinguished or influential members of the local authority community and test them.

As before, the shelters were built in a circle around a 250 kg German bomb buried 12 feet 6 inches deep, the nearest corner of each shelter being 15 feet from the bomb. Shelter No. 1 was a normal unreinforced brick shelter, the walls of which had been stiffened with earth banking to a height and width of 3 feet 6 inches all round the shelter. Shelter No. 2 was similar except that the banking was much more extensive and expensive. It had at the bottom a width of 4 feet 2 inches consisting of brick rubble faced at an angle of 60 degrees with 9 inch brickwork in lime mortar. Shelter No. 3 was a normal shelter with 2 inch by $\frac{3}{8}$ inch mild steel bars taken up the walls and over the roof slab, these flat bars being covered with expanded metal to form a key for cement rendering which covered them. Shelter No. 4 was a much more elaborate and impossibly expensive strengthening. The shelter had been given a complete reinforced concrete external skin with horizontal reinforcing rods $\frac{3}{8}$ inch diameter at 12 inch centres. Vertical chases had been cut into the brickwork at 5 feet intervals up which ran two $\frac{1}{2}$ inch diameter vertical rods, their lower ends were bolted to a 20 inch length of 4 inch by 2 inch steel channel placed horizontally in a chase cut right through the wall of the original shelter, while their upper ends passed through a length of 4 inch by 2 inch steel channel to which it was bolted, the channel passing right across the roof and being connected to the new vertical reinforcing rods on the other side. Shelter No. 5 was not unlike No. 4 except that there was no continuous reinforced concrete external skin, the strengthening system consisting of reinforced concrete external piers with steel straps in the form of channels running across the top of the shelter. Shelter No. 6 was a normal unreinforced type provided as a control.

The test took place on 19th June, 1941. It was in Richmond Park, London, and not at Stewartby. This made it easier to entertain not only those who had designed the shelters but a large and distinguished group of other City Engineers. The bomb went off and the debris rose in its now familiar, but always impressive, style and down the debris came again. When the dust and smoke had cleared there was a sorry sight, everything had disappeared but for one shelter and a bit of another. My Princes Risborough team were kindly men and women; they did not go forward with the visitors to inspect the debris. We knew pretty well what to expect. It can best be recounted in the words of the report on the proceedings from the Road Research Laboratory staff which appeared in July 1941. It says of Shelter No. 1—the roof was thrown clear of the shelter and the whole of the brickwork above the earth banking was destroyed. The walls left standing were badly shaken and the inside of the shelter was partly filled with debris. Shelter No. 2—the roof was thrown almost clear and only two short lengths of side walls were left standing. The whole of the inside of the shelter was filled with debris including rubble and bricks from the banking. Shelter No. 3—the roof was thrown clear of the shelter and the whole of the walls collapsed with the exception of one short length of one side wall. Some of the mild steel straps were fractured and some of the tie rods were dragged out of the chases in the floor. Shelter No. 4 with the reinforced concrete outer skin and steel channels across the top behaved very well. Apart from slight cracks in walls and roof it was little damaged. Shelter No. 5 suffered badly but did not collapse completely. The roof of Shelter No. 6, the control, was thrown clear and the shelter was almost completely destroyed.

RE4's designs for strengthening existing unreinforced shelters incorporated a continuous ductile skin either outside or inside the shelter. A series of these designs were built and tested in Richmond Park. Again the shelters were arranged in a circle with their nearest corner 15 feet from the buried 250 kg bomb. The strengthening of the first shelter was extremely simple. It consisted of an outer $4\frac{1}{2}$ inch thick brick skin built in cement mortar keyed with header bricks into the original shelter walls. Between the old wall and the new skin, BRC steel fabric reinforcement was placed. It was carried right over the roof where it was bedded in a 3 inch thick layer of concrete so wrapping the shelter in a continuous piece of fabric.

The second system provided an inner skin of 4 inch thick reinforced concrete, keyed at intervals to the existing brick wall. At every 4 feet horizontally a vertical reinforcing rod was carried through a hole punched in the existing roof, the end of the rod being screwed and secured to the top of the roof by means of a washer and nut. The lower end of this reinforcing rod was carried down into a hole chased into the road slab, on which the original shelter had been built, and was grouted into it.

The next shelter was very similar to the last except that the new reinforced concrete skin was not anchored to the road slab, it was separated from it by a layer of building paper so that slip might occur. The new work was keyed to the old and toes were provided through the existing brick wall at 4 feet centres into which the ends of the vertical reinforcement were turned.

There was a third and slightly more elaborate variation on this internal strengthening system. Instead of the vertical reinforcing rods being carried into the walls or fixed in pockets in the road slab, they were taken into a new 3 inch floor which was separated from the road slab by a layer of building paper, thus forming a ductile box structure instead of a portal.

Though these strengthening systems were not embarked upon with any great enthusiasm, they all proved under test remarkably successful. While there was very little to choose between them, the box form behaved marginally better though it was considerably more expensive than the others. Descriptions of all these methods of strengthening, or slight variations on them, were published in the Consolidated Circular. In that Circular will also be found the design of a complete box form reinforced concrete shelter. This also proved most satisfactory under test.

There were relatively few reports showing the behaviour of strengthened brick shelters in the blitz but one was remarkable. It occurred at Cowes on 4th May, 1942 when a very large 1000 kg bomb exploded 28 feet from the centre of a row of three 12 person public shelters, all occupied beyond their rated capacity, which had been strengthened in accordance with the Circular only two weeks before. The crater formed was 72 feet in diameter and 20 feet deep. All three shelters were initially in the crater area though they very rapidly moved distances of 10, 12 and 13 feet respectively from it. Shelter No. 1 was practically undamaged, the rendering over the emergency exit alone being slightly displaced. Shelter No. 2 was tilted away from the bomb, the walls were practically intact except for the concrete lintel over the entrance which cracked but remained in position. The roof was covered with a very heavy load of debris which caused it to crack. Shelter No. 3 was very severely shaken but all the occupants escaped uninjured. Three people who were standing between Shelters No. 1 and 2 were killed.

Enough has been said in this chapter about the early work on surface shelters but improvements continued to be made and to be tested. Colin Lucas, in a Minute dated 20 March, 1942 to Stradling, incidentally complaining that the Consolidated Circular to be published that month contained, in its turn, directives with which RE4 strongly disagreed, mentions tests Nos. 6, 7, 8 and 9 on surface shelters still to be carried out in Richmond Park.

From the beginning these tests had been popular, spectacular, shows which attracted distinguished visitors. To an early one at Stewartby I invited Miss Ellen Wilkinson, Chairman of the Shelter Policy Committee and members of her staff. The Rt. Hon. Ellen C. Wilkinson, PC, at that time Parliamentary Secretary to the Ministry of Home Security, was a great woman. In fact she was small and red headed, feminine enough to appreciate, and perhaps at times to be influenced by the charm of her 63 year old adviser, Sir Alexander Rouse who sat at her right hand in committee, but otherwise tough. She had been MP for the Jarrow Division of Durham since 1935 when she tramped almost the whole way from Jarrow to London on the famous march of her unemployed constituents. She was intrepid. One of the least popular duties for her Home Security staff was to be summoned to an evening "blitzing", when shelters and wardens posts were visited as near to the centre of the raid as possible. Miss Wilkinson had no fear but some of her companions were not so fortunately endowed.

At the Stewartby visit, after she and her party had inspected the circle of shelters, they were requested by the officer in charge to retire to a ridge about 200 yards away where we stationed our guests out of range of debris. Miss Wilkinson objected. She inferred that all the observers were lily-livered for wanting to move so far away and that I, in particular, as the designer of the new shelters, should show my confidence by sitting in one while the explosion took place. I was not to be drawn and insisted on moving her to the ridge. There we waited. The signal was given. The plunger of the electrical device which would detonate the bomb was forced down violently, but instead of the expected explosion and the impressive 250 foot high plume of debris rushing into the air, there came from the centre of the circle, out of the hole where the bomb was buried, a pathetic little puff of smoke. The bomb had failed to detonate completely.

This, of course, meant the end of the proceedings for that day since it was our usual practice on such occasions to allow some hours to elapse before removing the bomb—just in case. However this did not suit Ellen Wilkinson. She had travelled from London to the outskirts of Bedford and she had been cheated of her spectacle. She again picked on me, as the responsible party, making it clear that the least I could do for her was to dig out the bomb with my own hands, there and then, and substitute another.

CHAPTER 6

The Indoor Shelter

Quite early in the "phoney-war" period, soon after the wattle and earth designs were produced, as described in Chapter 2, attention was turned to providing shelter in the home. The most effective proposal came from D. C. Burn. It was a propping system for use in a ground floor room of a dwelling house, a stout frame made of timber, with four posts, one in each corner of the room, supporting four beams just below the ceiling, to which the posts were braced by diagonal members, all being bolted rigidly together. The idea was based on an intelligent anticipation of what enemy bombing was to prove later, that the bedroom floor of the typical villa was, in itself, a strong element quite capable of supporting the debris from the roof, chimney stack and upper walls if the house was shaken down by a near miss. The timber frame did nothing to protect the shelterers from collapse of the ground floor walls but it was a comforting addition, at that time, for any house that had no other shelter.

Burn, with a family of two small boys, built one himself and as our family of two girls was suddenly increased by the arrival of three little evacuees from Eastbourne I followed suit. These evacuees had had nasty experiences of bombing before leaving home but their nervousness was allayed by the stout timber props when a "protected room" was built to house them and their small hostesses. This propping was given official blessing being described in a Ministry Bulletin No. C14, in which the illustration showing the construction of a protective wall, was a photograph of our installation.

Since timber, in short supply, was needed for the frame they could not be provided in great numbers but there are records of 1365 rooms being strengthened in this way, of which 218 were destroyed mostly by fire. However later in the war, one in Exeter was to fulfil its purpose admirably. The propping had been erected in the back room of a two-storey semi-detached house built in 1892 with 9 inch external brick walls, timber floors and a slated roof. At 23.30 hours on 23rd April, 1942, a 500 kg bomb fell outside the house 27 feet from the corner of the propped room, forming a crater 10 feet deep and 30 feet in diameter. The house was completely demolished but the propping, which can be seen clearly, Fig. 6.1, did its job. It protected the occupants, one woman and two children who were in bed under it. They were unhurt, apart from a bruise on the woman's knee.

Though the Government Anderson shelter issued to householders for erection in their gardens was, as remarked earlier, structurally sound, it soon became clear that this form of shelter had been made ineffective by the change in the enemy's tactics. The Anderson was essentially a trench shelter and though it did not suffer from the structural defects of the standard concrete linings, since it was continuous and ductile, it shared all the other drawbacks of trenches. It would have been tolerable if the conditions envisaged when it was designed had continued, that is to say if the enemy raids had been of short duration. However, when the pattern of all-night alerts was established, as happened in

Fig. 6.1

London in September 1940, it was obvious that the Anderson shelter would be quite unsatisfactory when winter came. Each one of us who left London at the end of a day's work, from September onwards, filled his passenger seats with worried men, anxious to get to their suburban homes so that they could see their families safely installed in their garden shelters before night fell. When the shelters were cold holes in the ground, which would always be damp and often flooded in wet weather, the prospect of the long winter nights was not encouraging. Local authorities did what they could by providing bunks so that the shelterers could go to bed but nothing effective could be done to stop the flooding or even to reduce the damp. It was soon realised that there was a factor other than structural safety essential in shelter design and that was "occupancy factor". It was impossible to claim that a shelter was efficient, however small its vulnerable area, if its occupancy factor was zero, that is to say if no one would use it. There was every prospect that the Anderson shelter would come into this class with a resultant rise in casualties and a fall in morale.

None of this had been realised at the time of Mr. Morrison's visit to Princes Risborough and so no steps to provide more effective protection for the family had been taken in the programme of work described in the last chapter. We in the Design and Development Section, soon realised how serious this omission was and took steps to correct it. I approached the Chief Engineer's Branch with the proposal that a shelter should be designed to accommodate a family inside its own house. I did not submit a design but merely sought recognition that this new project should be added to the heavy load of design work already in hand which, it had been stipulated by the Minister, must be carried out in agreement with the Chief Engineer. No reply was made to this proposal. I persisted firmly but politely, in true civil service fashion, addressing Minutes to the Chief Engineer. Nothing happened for some weeks, then a reply was received. Unfortunately no copy has survived but I remember the gist of it vividly. It came from Mr. Osmond, a kindly and quite senior administrative officer in "O" Division. It said that no new project was to be undertaken since it was impossible to provide safe shelter inside a house; this had been established in 1938 by a panel of eminent engineers. I was referred to Command Paper 5932.

No one in RE4 had ever heard of the Command Paper. This may be a reflection on the efficiency of the Research and Experiments Department but it is also a sure indication of how our work had been limited. The Chief Engineer was responsible for shelters and therefore papers dealing with their design had not been brought to the notice of the scientific advisers, through the Civil Defence Research Committee or otherwise. On becoming heavily involved early in October in the design of shelters I should, of course, have taken immediate steps to seek out and study any literature relating to the subject. Needless to say I lost no time, after receiving Osmond's Minute, in obtaining a copy of the Command Paper.

It proved to be a document of the greatest interest, being nothing less than a Report on Air Raid Shelter Policy which had been, as the title page put it, "Presented by the Secretary of State for the Home Department to Parliament by Command of His Majesty, December, 1938". I had been amused by Osmond's use of the adjective "eminent" in his description of the panel of engineers: I had considered it merely a mild rebuke to a somewhat troublesome, pushing young man, but it was completely justified. The Report had been drawn up by David Anderson, doyen of British civil engineers, senior partner in the civil engineering consulting firm of Mott, Hay and Anderson, B. L. Hurst, the most successful consulting structural engineer of his time, senior partner in the consulting firm B. L. Hurst and Partners, and Sir Henry Japp, KBE, a leading contractor, chief engineer and works director of the civil engineering contracting firm of John Mowlem and Co. Ltd.

Though their Report deals briefly with the whole problem of the provision of shelters, it is mainly concerned, as its opening paragraph emphasises, with the sectional shelter. The term "sectional" is not defined but it is clear from the context that it refers to the heavy corrugated sheet steel arched sections which made up the trench lining, illustrated in Fig. 6.2, which was later issued to householders and popularly called the Anderson shelter, named not after David Anderson the engineer whom the public would not know, but after Sir John Anderson, the Lord Privy Seal to whom the Report was addressed.

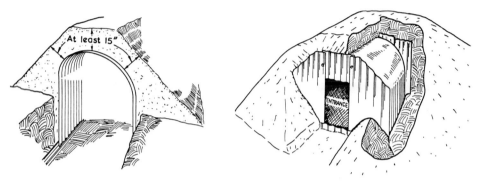

Fig. 6.2

The report was of such value to the Design and Development Section that that part dealing with the sectional shelter must be reproduced in full.

Report to the Lord Privy Seal

"We have had the opportunity of discussing with the Lord Privy Seal some of the problems of the shelter policy, and in particular the proposal to provide sectional shelters for the population of vulnerable areas in their own homes.

In the first place we would record our whole-hearted agreement with the Lord Privy Seal that the provision of a shelter in or in close proximity to the home of every citizen in vulnerable areas is a sound policy, and that such shelter should provide reasonable protection against blast and splinters from the near-by explosion of a medium-sized H.E. bomb and against the collapse of the super-structure, and we have now to record our opinion as to how far a sectional steel shelter can fulfil the requirements of this policy.

I(a) A sectional steel device is one method of providing such shelter. There are a number of such devices on the market and we consider that two or three standard types could be adopted which would satisfy the requirements and which would enable a large number of firms to adapt their plant to the production of one or other of the types with the least possible delay.

(b) Such a shelter should measure not less than 6 feet by 4 feet 6 inches in plan and should not be less than 6 feet high from the crown of the arch to the floor. This shelter would hold four persons for a short period and might even in an emergency hold six persons. It would, therefore, form the minimum shelter for the two-storeyed terraced house or cottage type of modern house, which on the average, accommodates rather under four persons. The dimensions given are in our opinion the absolute minimum for three reasons:

(i) Anything smaller would have no market value above its value as scrap, whereas a structure of the minimum size which we recommend would have a definite value for other useful purposes.

(ii) That there would be serious risk of very rapid suffocation in any smaller shelter in the event of the exits being blocked and

(iii) Anything smaller would be unacceptable to the people and we would particularly emphasise the danger of issuing a type of shelter which could only be entered by crawling and in which only a crouching or recumbent attitude is possible.

(c) The weight of such a shelter would be from 5 cwt to 7 cwt.

II With regard to the position to be occupied by these shelters we are definitely opposed to the placing of them within houses for the following reasons:

(a) The ordinary ground floor room of the small house only measures about 10 feet by 12 feet and therefore such a room would be to all intents and purposes out of action whilst the shelter was in it. Every air raid will reduce the available accommodation and increase the pressure on undamaged houses in already overcrowded areas, and it is therefore an error to render any accommodation useless for normal purposes.

(b) The shelter would provide no additional protection against splinters beyond that which the walls of the room provide, and would have no resistance to splinters entering through the doors or windows.

(c) Unless the floor of the room were removed and the shelter placed on the ground below (generally about 15 inches below the floor) there is danger of the shelter being driven through the floor by the collapse of the house, to the added danger of the occupants.

(d) Unless the shelter were strongly anchored to the floor, the collapse of one side of the house would incur the risk of its displacement and distortion.

(e) There is a very serious risk of debris from the fall of the house forming a solid wedge of masonry at the ends of the shelter making the rescue of the occupants very difficult. For the same reason there is a risk of the occupants being suffocated from lack of air and by the dust from the debris. The higher the house the greater will be this risk.

(f) Assuming, as seems most likely, that an attack with H.E. bombs will be accompanied by the use of incendiary bombs, the risk that the shelter will become an oven for the trapped occupants is a very real one and one which we consider would render the acceptance by the people of the device for use inside a house more than doubtful.

(g) There is a risk that the entrapped occupants may be killed by the escape of gas from the domestic supply (the gas-mask is not proof against this form of gas).

A shelter device of this kind, to be provided in large numbers must in our judgement satisfy public opinion. Undoubtedly most people would prefer to stay in their houses to take shelter, and though at first sight the device might seem to render this possible, the plain truth is that if they do so, within the protection of such a shelter, their chances of rescue are greatly diminished and the prospect of a lingering death increased if the house collapses. Ease of exit is the most fundamental requirement of a proper shelter and ease of exit from a sectional shelter within a small collapsed house is almost a contradiction in terms.

There is, however, in our judgement a very definite place in the shelter policy for a steel shelter device of this kind for small houses. During the recent crisis the Home Office recommendation that the householder should dig a trench in the back-yard or garden was severely criticised on the grounds that many could not afford the cost of the materials necessary to revet the trench, and there was a demand for the free issue of material for the purpose.

The sectional device is an answer to this criticism. Placed in the garden or yard and covered with earth or sandbags it provides as good a shelter as a covered trench. It should be sunk at least partially in the ground as this not only provides increased lateral protection but also provides the earth necessary to cover the shelter. Thus protected it can be placed close to the house without serious risk from the collapse of the building."

This report was of such interest and value, not so much because it came down so firmly against placing the shelters within houses, but because the reasons for this decision were set down in Section II.

The first step in design is to define the problem, to state clearly the aim and object of the exercise, then to list any constraints and other difficulties that must be overcome. The eminent authors had defined the problem completely and set out the difficulties and objections clearly in the seven paragraphs of Section II and the comments that followed. All that the designer in 1940 had to do was to consider these seven objections and to find ways of overcoming them. He had two powerful advantages over the panel working in 1938. He had the evidence of the full scale experiments being provided daily by the enemy and he was not constrained by the elastic theory of structures. I was confident that with these advantages we could design an efficient open frame structure and so reverse the panel's decision. Mr. Osmond was so informed but he did not relent. Then on 1st December, 1940, the Chief Engineer of the Ministry of Home Security telephoned from Whitehall and a conversation something like this took place.

"Baker, we'll have to do something about an indoor shelter, the Prime Minister is on our track. Will you come up and help me choose one?"

"What do you mean, choose one?"

"Oh! We've got dozens of designs here, every Tom, Dick and Harry in the country has suggested something."

"I certainly won't come and choose one; give me a day or two and I'll bring up the plans of a shelter which has really been designed to behave properly."

The gist of this conversation stayed clearly in my mind because Rouse's request seemed so odd. Though socially we remained on good terms our professional relationship had been under some strain since October while the standard shelters were being redesigned by RE4, an activity which could be considered a criticism of the Chief Engineer's earlier work and of his authority. Yet here he was appealing to me, who claimed to possess the secret of efficient design and who had been pressing for months for the opportunity to produce an indoor shelter, to come and help choose some amateur's effort.

It is certainly the last thing I would have done in similar circumstances. Nevertheless I went up to London a few days later with a sketch design of an open frame structure and showed it to Rouse, an administrative officer of "O" Division named Hutson and others. The design was not received with any enthusiasm for the simple reason that a shelter had already been selected and a mock-up was already standing in the corridor outside. It was a steel shelter, in cross-section the shape of a Gothic arch, with ribs of bent rolled-steel section covered with quarter inch thick steel plate and with steel plate flaps closing the ends. It obviously did not satisfy any of the specifications for an indoor shelter. It was, in effect, a sectional shelter which the Command Paper had rightly described as a death trap. Quite apart from this it was of such complexity that it could not have been mass produced easily and cheaply, as a Government issue shelter would have to be to meet the emergency then facing the country

I pointed out all these shortcomings quite forcibly but to no purpose. I was baffled. To jump to it and reconsider the problem of the indoor shelter when instructed by the Prime Minister whatever difficulties were involved was proper enough, but to produce a solution which ran absolutely counter to the advice of that Panel of eminent engineers, which up to that moment had been used to block all action, passed belief.

As soon as our meeting broke up, Rouse's personal assistant told me what had happened. Apparently, Mr. Churchill, a few days before, concerned as he would be at the hardships of the common people and the possible danger to the war effort of any serious drop in their morale, had said to Mr. Morrison, "Herbert, you must give the people a shelter in their own homes", then, not for the last time, he had gone too far with his instructions and said "Something like this", taking an envelope from his pocket and drawing on it an inverted U shape. This was immediately and indelibly printed on the bureaucratic mind so, from the amateur designs available, one as close as possible in outline to the Prime Minister's arch diagram had been chosen. My sketch design had a flat top, so it was automatically ruled out. However, I knew that the Gothic arch shelter would be a fiasco and must be stopped, so I returned to Princes Risborough to complete our design. The steps involved are easily retraced.

If the extracts from the Command Paper are studied (page 45) it will be seen that the main objection to placing a sectional shelter inside a house was the fear that the occupants might be trapped by the debris when the house collapsed. This is stressed in paragraphs II(e), (f), (g) and in the following paragraph which ends with the sentence "Ease of exit is the most fundamental requirement of a proper shelter and ease of exit from a sectional shelter within a small collapsed house is almost a contradiction in terms". Anything like a sectional shelter with only one exit was therefore out of the question. Debris might flow on to a shelter from any direction so, to give the shelterers the best possible chance of escape exits must be provided on all four sides.

This postulated an open frame structure, something like the frame for a single-storey steel framed building or the portals tested at Bristol. Why had the authors of the Command Paper not considered this form? They could only work within the limitations of their time and so were confined to a consideration of elastic behaviour. Had they thought in terms of absorbing the energy of the collapsing house they must, for reasons set out in Chapter 4, have considered the open frame solution impracticable. The potential energy of a typical two-storey villa, or cottage type of modern house as the panel archaically described it, is equivalent to about 150 tons falling 10 feet. To absorb this energy which is released by the falling house, without exceeding the yield stress of the steel would have required so heavy a frame that, quite apart from expense, it could not have been carried into the villa. The authors had, unfortunately, no experiments to suggest to them that a smaller value for the energy might be justified or that a frame could be made to absorb it safely.

Our next step was to decide the overall dimensions of the shelter. The key to this lay in paragraph II(a) which warned that space would be at a premium once raiding began. The obvious reply was to make the shelter a useful article of furniture so that it would not put the room out of action, and even to go further and make it dual purpose so that it would actually economise in space. This was done by making it a bed by night and a table by day. The usual size of a double bed is 6 feet 6 inches by 4 feet 6 inches and the height of a dining table is 2 feet 6 inches and so the dimensions were fixed. This is a great moment in an engineer's day when he can draw lines on his paper defining the shape and overall dimensions of his structure. However it does not settle for him the sizes of the members which will make up his structure. For this, it will be remembered from Chapter 4, an estimate of the energy to be absorbed is first required. Here the 1940 designer had the great advantage that, even by the end of that year, he could draw on an immense amount of experimental evidence. The German bombs that, as near misses, had shaken down houses showed that one part was surprisingly strong; that was the bedroom floor, consisting of timber joists to which the floor-boards were securely nailed. It almost always fell in one piece, either more or less horizontally if all the walls collapsed together or, more usually, hingeing about one edge when only the walls nearest the bomb went. This latter was the most rigorous condition since the entire impact might be carried by only one top longitudinal member of the shelter and the blow would be inclined to the vertical, whereas a horizontal fall would be taken straight on to the vertical legs. The floor, having been brought to rest by the shelter, was in a position to protect it from the impact of further falls of roof and upper walls.

A typical room would not exceed 14 feet in span and 9 feet in height with the weight of floor and bedroom furniture 20 lb per square foot. The total energy of that part of the falling floor to strike the shelter was thus calculated to be 142 000 inch-lb. For a preliminary design, to be checked by subsequent test, it was assumed that only one half of this energy need be absorbed by the shelter the rest going into the floor below and elsewhere. For reasons that will be obvious from the argument of Chapter 4 it was decided to provide rigid joints between the horizontal and vertical members. For further economy the greatest possible permanent deflection (OM in Fig. 4.7) had to be allowed. Since the shelter was to be 2 feet 6 inches high it was considered that the top horizontal members could deflect at their centres by 12 inches without causing injury to even the stoutest occupant, always assuming he was lying down—if he was not when the bomb exploded he certainly would be by the time the house collapsed. From these dimensions and assumptions it was calculated that a structural steel member $\frac{1}{4}$ inch thick, in the shape of an angle with one leg 3 inches long and the other 2 inches (i.e) a 3 inch by 2 inch by $\frac{1}{4}$ inch angle, would be more than adequate. To confirm this a shelter was constructed and placed on a concrete slab, which would absorb less energy than any normal ground floor. A timber joisted floor 14 feet long and 5 feet 3 inches wide weighing 20 lb per square foot was erected 9 feet above the slab and, hingeing about a short edge, was allowed to fall on the shelter. The permanent deflection of the 3 inch by 2 inch horizontal member was only $6\frac{1}{4}$ inches instead of the 8 inches which had been estimated.

The final design of the frame is shown in Fig. 6.3 where it will be seen that the rigid joints were obtained by bending steel plate around the corners and attaching them to the ends of the horizontal members and to the vertical member, which was $2\frac{1}{2}$ inch by $2\frac{1}{2}$ inch by $\frac{1}{4}$ inch angle, with two $\frac{3}{4}$ inch diameter bolts, 2.75 inches apart.

While the steel framework alone would protect the shelterers from the falling floor it would not prevent them from being suffocated by the dust and debris that would follow

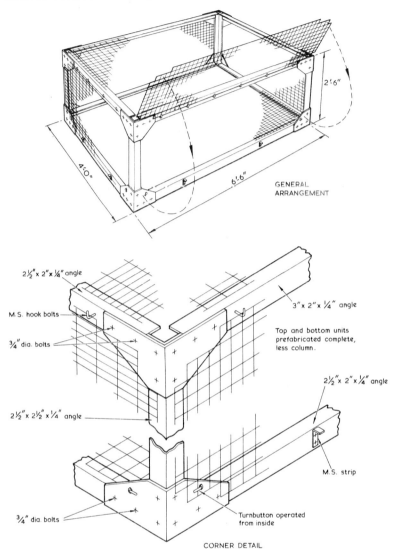

GENERAL
ARRANGEMENT

2½" x 2" x ¼" angle

M.S. hook bolts

¾" dia. bolts

3" x 2" x ¼" angle

Top and bottom units
prefabricated complete,
less column.

2½" x 2" x ¼" angle

2½" x 2½" x ¼" angle

M.S. strip

¾" dia. bolts

Turnbutton operated
from inside

CORNER DETAIL

MORRISON SHELTER – PRELIMINARY DESIGN

Fig. 6.3

the explosion. The framework had, therefore, to be clothed with some form of protective panelling. This had to be of open mesh construction first because any light sheet material, such as corrugated iron, would be blown violently into the shelter by nearby blast and secondly on hygienic grounds since four people were likely to occupy the shelter for hours at a stretch. A great hunt, conducted by D. C. Burn, revealed no suitable fibre or fabric netting but it did confirm that steel "weld mesh", made of high tensile wire arranged in a rectangular mesh welded at every intersection, a material commonly used as reinforcement for concrete roads, was ideal. It was rigid enough to be handled as a panel, requiring no frame, and it was immensely strong. It was decided that nothing else would do and that a fight would be made for a sufficient quantity, not only for the side panels but also for the bottom, acting as a mattress, and for the top. This top might not appear strong enough but, when bolted around all four edges to the top angles of the shelter, tests showed that it would hold up any block of brickwork that might be blown on to the shelter. It was, in fact, in common with the side panels and bottom, strong enough in impact to develop the full strength of the main angle members to which it was attached and there was no point therefore in looking for something stronger. It remained, of course, for the householder to show some initiative and provide plywood or linoleum as a covering when he wished to use the shelter as a table.

The side panels were loosely hung on steel hooks screwed into the top angle, the lower line of wire just passing under a steel (MS) strip angle screwed to the bottom member and shown in Fig. 6.3. When debris was thrown against the panel, it bent inwards. This brought the top and bottom wires hard up against the hooks at the top and the steel strip angles at the bottom so that the vertical wires of the mesh were thrown into tension and successfully kept all debris out. As the shelterers tucked themselves up for the night they operated from inside the shelter a turn button, shown in Fig. 6.3. This kept the panels tight up against the framework ready to receive debris. It had the additional advantage that it prevented anyone falling out of bed if the shelter was crowded, or, to be less flippant, if the shelter was moved violently by an explosion. A turn of the button in the morning released the panel which swung up about the top row of hooks allowing exit from all four sides. When the shelter was to be used as a table the panels were merely lifted off the top hooks and stored elsewhere. If in a severe bomb incident the shelter was completely surrounded by debris it would be relatively easy for the rescue squad, equipped with wire cutters, to make the necessary escape hole in the mesh panels.

It is interesting at this point, to turn back to the Command Paper to see how far the design meets the seven objections set out there. It does so in the following way:

(a) The shelter has a secondary use as a table, what is more, being open framed it does not cut down light to any part of the room.

(b) War-time experience had already shown that the walls of the normal house were sufficient protection against splinters. The shelter had to be so positioned that a bomb fragment would have to penetrate at least one wall. For example, it should not be placed in front of a French window. The height of the shelter prevented the occupants from rising above window sill level.

(c) The design incorporates a firmly attached bottom independent of the floor of the room. There would be no danger to the occupants, or to the shelter, if it were driven through the floor.

(d) There is little risk to the occupants from displacement; care had been taken to avoid large flat vertical surfaces for blast to act on. The basic principle underlying the design of the structure was to allow large distortion.

(e), (f) and (g) refer to the danger of trapping. The danger of this had been minimised by supplying easy exit in every direction. If the occupants could not escape immediately they ran no danger of suffocation since the side panels prevented debris covering them. Dust certainly would be present but war-time experience had already shown that if anyone trapped had their hands free and so could cover their faces, as they instinctively did, this was sufficient to prevent injury from dust. The risk from fire was not serious; the dust and debris thrown up were most effective in putting out fires. Escaping gas from the domestic supply might certainly be a danger and could only be minimised by providing all possible escape routes.

The Design and Development Section worked extremely hard with their search for materials and their preliminary tests, so that the final design of the shelter was ready in not much longer time than has been taken in writing down the account of its progress. This was fortunate because I, who was not without friends in the Chief Engineer's Department in Whitehall, was warned that the prototype arch shelter, a mock-up of which had been on view early in December, was to be taken to Downing Street at 12 noon on 31st December to be inspected by the Prime Minister. I felt that argument, however firmly it was backed by theory and design, was no match for this direct action. The only way to counter it was to produce a better article for the layman to see and touch. I therefore decided to build a table shelter and to get it into Downing Street somehow.

The Forest Products Research Laboratory workshops were enthusiastic with their help. They secured the necessary material in a remarkably short time and had a full-sized shelter built and loaded on a lorry by the early morning of 31st December. So we set off with it to London without any firm plan. We were allowed to drive into Downing Street without any questions being asked. There, outside No. 10, stood the dignified figure of Sir Alexander Rouse supervising in person the transport of the arch shelter into the house. I approached him. Sir Alexander said cheerfully "Hello, what are you doing here?" "I've brought the Ministry of Home Security Indoor Shelter," I replied.

Rouse looked ruefully into the lorry, paused for a horrifyingly long minute and then said, resignedly but cheerfully, "Oh, well, you'd better bring it in."

So the table shelter was carried into No. 10, across the hall into a room on the left, where it joined its rival.

Walking down Whitehall back to Rouse's office in the Home Office building, I asked when the Prime Minister was to be shown the shelters.

"At 5 o'clock," said Rouse "but there is no need for you to be there." I remonstrated pointing out that no one else knew anything about the design and that a rectangular steel box by itself was not likely to impress the Prime Minister or anyone else. But Rouse would not give way. It may very well have been outside his power to add anyone to the deputation. I did not realise this at the time and unkindly put the refusal down to baser motives, and so kept on nagging. By this time we were in his office and the request was referred to some higher authority, perhaps the Permanent Secretary, or even to the Minister himself. Eventually the instruction came down that "Professor Baker could go to Downing Street but he was on no account to speak to Mr. Churchill." This struck me as an amusing restriction but I did not quarrel with it. Just as I was leaving the office a messenger came in to say that the meeting with the Prime Minister had been postponed until 6.0 p.m.

Over lunch I had an unworthy thought. Was it possible that this message was a put-up job? Was the Headquarters team so keen on getting their arch shelter approved that they would be glad if there was no one present at 5.0 p.m. to explain the table model? Frankly, I thought they might. Diffidence prevented me taxing them with this so I decided to play the idiot child. I presented myself at the door of No. 10 soon after 4.30 p.m. A uniformed messenger opened the door. I said that I had to demonstrate one of the shelters brought in that morning but could not remember whether it was to be at 5.0 or 6.0 p.m. Could the messenger find out?

"No" said he "but you can come in and wait", indicating an old-fashioned canopied watchman's chair. There I sat for upwards of an hour and a half (my base suspicions had been groundless) and watched enthralled while war leaders and statesmen went in and out. Eventually Mr. Herbert Morrison, Rouse and Hutson arrived. We went into the room where the shelters were.

Morrison was shown the arch type and then noticed the table shelter. There was just time to tell him about it, explaining the principles underlying the design when Mr. Churchill, accompanied by Admiral Sir Roger Keyes, Commander-in-Chief of the recently formed Combined Operations Force, entered the room.

The Prime Minister looked magnificent, fresh complexioned and buoyant, a great contrast to the last time I had seen him in the summer of 1939. That occasion was a Degree Congregation dinner at Bristol University. Mr. Churchill, as Chancellor of the University, had proposed the toast of the chief guest, Mr. Kennedy, the United States Ambassador. Churchill made one of his great speeches, an impassioned plea for the two great English speaking nations to go hand-in-hand down the dangerous road of the future. Kennedy had, no doubt, already written Britain off as a dead loss. At all events his reply was a conventional little speech which ignored everything Churchill had said. The comparison between the two men, as the high-table guests filed out in procession, was striking. Kennedy then was the one who looked fresh complexioned and buoyant, while Churchill was bowed and grey complexioned as if he realised that his cry had once more gone unheeded. Perhaps he knew too that many of the diners, narrow little academics that we were, disapproved of their Chancellor taking such an opportunity to make what they took to be a political speech instead of talking about "the need for poets", or some such scholarly topic, as Chancellor Stanley Baldwin had recently done at Cambridge.

After the introductions Morrison said, indicating the arch shelter:

"There you are, Prime Minister, that's the kind of thing you wanted." Churchill went and sat on the edge of the table shelter, which he obviously thought was a piece of furniture, and looked approvingly at the poor arched object. Nothing much else occurred until Morrison said, "By the way, you are sitting on another one."

The Prime Minister got up and turned around to look at what he had been sitting on while Morrison proceeded, in a most impressive way, to recount all that he had been told about a structure that he had neither seen nor heard of until ten minutes earlier.

The Prime Minister listened and then turned to Rouse and said "But this is not as strong as an arch, is it?"

Rouse sensibly passed the question to me, I explained, what the reader already knows, that the problem was not so much one of strength as of energy absorption. This interested the Prime Minister who continued to question me and no one, of course, remembered the injunction forbidding me to speak. He was quick to appreciate all the points that had influenced the design as set out above. These rather blackened what reputation the arch, or sectional, shelter may have had and it was not looked at again. However, the merits of the table shelter were thoroughly thrashed out until Churchill, thumping the top of it vigorously so that the weld-mesh panels rattled, said, "This is the one. Make half a million in the next three months. Give them to the people. Show them that it is safe. Blow a house up on one. Put a pig in it, put the inventor in it," poking me playfully in the ribs.

So that was that; the day was won. But the interview was not over. The party became social and for half an hour Churchill and everyone relaxed, except the poor civil servant Hutson who had been silent and spellbound throughout. The conversation kept mainly to engineering topics with a distinctly nautical flavour. It was not too serious. One of the Prime Minister's sallies was, pointing to the table shelter, "It wouldn't take much to design that; not like designing a warship." I had to admit that it had not been quite as complicated a task as designing a warship.

Just as the party was breaking up after the most memorable hour of my professional life, Morrison made a remark which might have caused endless trouble, and was not worthy of so astute a man. He must have felt that, in being deprived of his arched shape, the Prime Minister had been slighted, for he said, "I tell you what, Prime Minister, we can have two shelters. This one with a flat top and a new arched one. I am sure Baker can design one to be as satisfactory as the other. Then the housewife can have her choice."

I felt that it was no moment to argue, so I weakly acquiesced. What a prospect it would have been had a choice been available, what complications for the supply department and what confusion for the housewife who was not practised in sizing up the relative merits of air-raid shelters. I knew that if the dangers of the sectional shelter were to be avoided the only way of doing what had been asked would be to substitute for the flat top of the table a piece of corrugated iron bent in arch form. This seemed rather silly, but, in the weeks that followed, we did make some attempt to produce an acceptable design, then quietly forgot it. As far as is known, no official enquiry was ever made about the proposal.

The day may have been won, but unfortunately even the Prime Minister's instruction to make half a million in three months did not automatically produce the materials for the job. The first trouble was over the supply of wire. The "weld-mesh" or BRC fabric used to cover all the faces of the shelter was made of wire. Apparently all wire in war-time belonged to the Admiralty who were not anxious to part with any. Home Security was told that no wire could be made available and considerable pressure was brought to bear on me to used some other sheet material. This pressure I resisted. Those days of working with the supply department of the Ministry of Home Security were not pleasant ones. There was no feeling of co-operating to produce the best possible shelter. Whenever a deadlock was reached the attitude at Headquarters was, "Well, Baker, that puts your shelter out". It would have been better if the reaction had been "that puts *our* shelter out". However, as every innovator must, I persevered. I was so convinced that "weld-mesh" was the only material for our purpose that I eventually persuaded the authorities to supply enough wire to make the side panels or screens. The further problems were then realised to be too big for Home Security's own supply department so I moved to the Ministry of Supply's Steel Control, which was situated at Ashorne Hill, a house near Leamington Spa, to argue the case.

This was a more relaxed atmosphere. I was alone dealing with steel people; however, we were not out of the wood, a problem of real magnitude faced us. The shelter had been designed throughout so that it could be easily mass produced but an order for half a million needed an amount of material that was staggering. For instance 15 million feet of one size of steel angle $2\frac{1}{2}$ inch by 2 inch by $\frac{1}{4}$ inch was required. It was soon broken to me that such a quantity could not be produced in three months if all the rolling mills in the country were put to work on it alone. The same happened with nuts and bolts of which 32 million of one size, $\frac{3}{4}$ inch diameter, were needed. The Steel Control staff, who obviously thought the whole project entertaining, were delightful. When we reached an impasse and it was decided to redesign the structure to fit the materials that were available I was provided with an aide-de-camp. We sat together in a small room which seemed to be full of telephones connected to the Director of small angles, the Director of big angles, of nuts, bolts, strip and every other conceivable variety of steel product. These directors could say at once what quantities of their particular product would be available within the next three months and so the redesign began.

Such an exercise would have been impossible in any reasonable time if the original design had not been completely rational. It would have been extremely difficult if the design had been based on elastic behaviour. What made it possible was that being based on plastic theory it could be assumed that larger meant better, that is to say that if a member were replaced by a larger one then the collapse load of the structure would be increased.

There were some great strokes of luck, due in the main to the availability of stocks of material not in demand in war-time. The most fruitful find was the stock of 6 inch by 6 inch by $\frac{3}{8}$ inch angle. This large member was available for the four table legs. It was wide enough to accommodate the two bolts at the ends of the top and bottom rails. This meant, not only that the eight expensive bent plate gussets could be dispensed with but that the number of $\frac{3}{4}$ inch diameter bolts could be halved, a saving of a cool 16 million.

Another piece of luck was the provision of solid plate for the top. Apparently some civil servant had been sent to America at the beginning of the war to secure supplies of steel for the ship-building industry. Among his purchases were acres of plate $\frac{1}{8}$ inch thick. Unfortunately no one had told him that nothing less than one quarter inch plate was used by British shipbuilders. Something that could not have been contemplated in the original shelter design because of its extravagance was thus willingly provided. The plate made a good firm top for the dinner-table and having solid steel above his head gave the shelterer more confidence. A brilliant solution to the problem of the expensive hooks from which, in the original design, the side panels were to hang, was provided by an anonymous member of Steel Control. The hooks were replaced by a row of eight $\frac{1}{4}$ inch bolts one inch long carrying a one inch diameter washer which was kept hard up against the head of the bolt by a $\frac{5}{16}$ inch length of $\frac{11}{32}$ inch bore ferrule as shown in the inset to Fig. 6.4 which illustrates the shelter as issued to the public. The top horizontal length of wire in a side panel rested on the ferrule passing through the $\frac{1}{4}$ inch bolt. An exactly similar row of bolts, washers and ferrules was inserted in the bottom rail of the shelter, so positioned that the bottom horizontal length of wire in the side panel just cleared the lower edge of the washer. When debris struck the panel it bent inwards and brought this bottom length of wire hard up against the ferrule on the bolt so that the full tensile strength of the vertical wires could be developed to resist the pressure of the debris. The brilliance of this simple piece of production engineering was that it enabled the side panel to be opened by hingeing not only about its top edge but, alternatively, about its bottom edge. If, when in place, the panel was moved upwards in its own plane until the bottom wire came hard up against the ferrule, then when it was swung outwards about this bottom edge, the top horizontal wire just cleared the washers on the top row of $\frac{1}{4}$ inch diameter bolts and the panel opened. When debris surrounded the shelter most escapes were made this way and it is sad that the identity of the designer who suggested this great improvement is not known. The expensive turn-button arrangement of the prototype (Fig. 6.3) for keeping the panel hard up against the frame of the shelter was replaced by a cheap and simple wire hook and eye fastening joining the lower corners of adjacent panels inside the shelter as shown in Fig. 6.4.

The only item which remained to be redesigned was the mattress, for which weld-mesh was not available. This proved the most difficult problem and the only one which caused me real anxiety. The purpose of the mattress was not only to give the occupants some

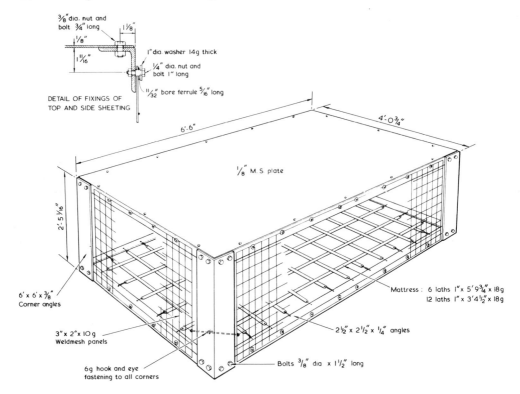

MORRISON SHELTER : FINAL DESIGN

Fig. 6.4

degree of comfort when lying quietly in the shelter but to contain them when the shelter was moved in an incident. The most severe test would come when the shelter was driven through the floor of the house and the mattress would be called upon to protect the occupants from the jagged broken floor boards. A promising suggestion was to return to the Victorian lath mattress which was formed by interlaced laths made of lengths of thin strip steel one inch wide. I liked this and produced a neat and economical way of securing the ends. These were bent through a right angle and held in place by the $\frac{1}{4}$ inch diameter bolts provided, as described above, to secure the bottom of the side panel, as shown in the two-tier shelter of Fig. 6.5. This produced a comfortable and immensely strong mattress. Unfortunately there was a sad snag, which well illustrates the complexity of engineering design problems. The steel strip had to be bent at the steel works, the distance between the bends being critical. Identical laths with bent ends would not "bundle" conveniently. That is to say they would not fit snugly together to form small neat bundles. I was informed by those responsible for transport that there were not enough railway trucks available to carry the awkward bundles of the many millions of bent laths required. This was hard to believe but the experts were adamant and so the mattress was made of straight lath with a hole punched at each end through which wire attachments, a plain hook at one end and a hook and small spring at the other, were fixed, their other ends passing through holes in

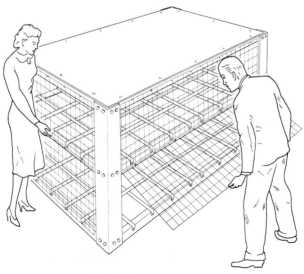

Fig. 6.5

the horizontal leg of the bottom rails. This provided a satisfactory mattress for sleeping on but there was no way of making absolutely certain that it would behave perfectly when driven through a floor. The problem was not amenable to calculation and there was no time to carry out elaborate tests. However, unpalatable as it was, the decision had to be made. In fact, as a later chapter will reveal, though there were many incidents in which the mattress disintegrated when driven through a floor, the end wire hooks being pulled out of their holes, they hung on just long enough to protect the occupants and there was no evidence of injury from this cause.

With the helpful co-operation of the members of Steel Control this work of redesigning was completed in less than a week. It resulted in a structure retaining all the principles embodied in that taken to Downing Street, except for slight reservations about the mattress, but differing radically in detail. It was a structure for which the materials were available to make half a million within the next three months and one simple enough for mass production without taxing the resources of the steel fabricating industry or straining the tax payer excessively, yet efficient enough to save the occupants of any house reduced to ruins by a near-miss.

When this position had been reached, the Chief Engineer and others from Home Security came to Ashorne Hill where they met members of Steel Control around a table and in a few minutes the results of the hectic week's work were blessed and the necessary agreements initialled.

One other important step remained to be taken at Princes Risborough. From the discussions at Ashorne Hill it was clear that the target date of three months could not be met unless a multitude of small workshops, even those attached to village garages, were brought in as fabricators. Most of them were incapable of building a complete shelter so the work was broken down and farmed out to those able to deal with individual parts. This meant that the parts had to be dimensioned so that, wherever they came from, they could be fitted together by unskilled labour, usually by Boy Scout volunteers. The structure was basically simple but it was made of stout, intractable material; brute force would not help if the various holes through which a bolt had to fit did not register and if, when the main structure was erected, the side panels did not swing easily between their upper and lower fixings. This demanded careful calculation of what the engineer calls "tolerances", the definition of the limits within which the length of a member or the position of a hole must lie. This was put into the hands of Leader-Williams and this meant that the job was perfectly done so that there were no troubles in erection.

There was certainly no trouble over the dimensions of the parts but the production phase had only just got under way when reports came through of trouble experienced in the small workshops. The holes for the $\frac{3}{4}$ inch diameter bolts were not drilled out of the structural steel angles, they were sheared out by a punch, a hard steel cylindrical tool provided by the Ministry, which was driven violently through the member so pushing out a small cylinder of steel, thus making the necessary hole. The trouble reported was that the punches were fracturing. Enquiry showed that the steel of the angles was harder than the punches. Further enquiry revealed the awful fact that these structural members were not being rolled from normal structural steel but from an inferior material, known as "shell discard". This was that part of the steel ingot in which all the impurities collected, so that it was not suitable even for turning into shells. It was not good enough to fire from guns but it was good enough apparently to be made into shelters. It was, most certainly, not good enough. Shell discard steel was brittle and made a complete travesty of the indoor shelter. I was shocked. To issue an indoor table shelter designed on the principles of continuity and ductility which was, in fact, brittle was an act that did not bear contemplation. I made no enquiry of how it had happened or who was responsible. It may have been on one side an over zealous steel "salesman" anxious to find a use for this unpopular steel or, on the other, someone supremely ignorant. Nothing useful would come of a witch hunt. All my energies were concentrated on correcting the error and, when the enormity of it was explained, everyone supported me so that, with the surprising speed that can be developed in war-time, it was arranged that every consignment of steel for the shelters should be tested by independent engineers to ensure that it was ductile. After this, all went smoothly. In little more than the three months mentioned in Downing Street the half million had been delivered and shortly afterwards were saving lives as will be described in the next chapter.

However, this chapter must not be closed without another glance at the two-tier shelter of Fig. 6.5. It was issued in small numbers to households with very large families but they did not call it into being. What happened was that in the early days of the issue of standard shelters an indignant letter was received accusing the Ministry of Home Security of encouraging immorality by issuing a double-bed for use by a household which might consist of a man and his housekeeper. The retort was an immediate order for the design of a two-tier shelter. This presented no problem and, since the number to be built was small, allowed the original lath mattress to be used, a matter of considerable satisfaction to me.

The shelter that has been described in this chapter was known officially as the "Table (Morrison) Indoor Shelter" and popularly as the "Morrison". Donoughue and Jones in their book *Portrait of a Politician*[1] attributed this, and the story carried by the press early in 1941 that Mr. Morrison himself invented the new shelter, to the inspiration of Clem Leslie, Morrison's faithful public relations officer. This may well have been so but it seemed to us in RE4 quite natural that, just as the sectional shelter had been called after Anderson the first Minister of Home Security, the new shelter should be called after the

[1] Bernard Donoughue and G. W. Jones, *Herbert Morrison—Portrait of a Politician*, Weidenfeld & Nicolson, London, 1973.

second. Morrison himself was in no doubt who was responsible for he wrote con-gratulating me in 1943, when I resigned from my post in his Ministry to take up new duties as Head of the Department of Engineering at Cambridge, saying generously "If the shelter that has become associated with my name were the only result of your work the country would have had cause to be grateful to you." However, some years later he was not quite so certain. When towards the end of 1950 I was about to appear before the Royal Commission on Awards to Inventors, as described in Chapter 12, I felt that I would like to let Mr. Morrison know what was in the wind. By good fortune I saw that he was to address one of the University political clubs in Cambridge towards the end of the Michaelmas Term. After the meeting I went along to the University Arms Hotel, where he was staying, and found him sitting alone in the lounge. He soon remembered who I was but when I told him that I was about to make a bid for an award for the design of the indoor shelter he nonplussed me by saying "But I thought I designed it myself."

There is no doubt that hardware associated with his name for a long period leaves an impression on a politician. Years later when attending a dinner at the Dorchester Hotel, London, I found myself sitting next to Lord Waverley, formerly Sir John Anderson. I did not imagine that my name on the guest list would have conveyed anything to him but during the soup course he turned to me and said:

"You had something to do with the Morrison shelter, didn't you?" I admitted that this was so. After a long pause, and not until the fish course, he said:

"It wasn't any good, was it?"

Though it seemed out of character, I thought he was pulling my leg gently so I said gaily:

"It was marvellous, the most successful structure ever to be designed."

"Nonsense," he replied irascibly, "it was usless. I should have opposed its adoption at the time but I thought it politically inexpedient."

CHAPTER 7

Morrison Incidents

The first recorded incidents, Cases 10a and 10b Table 7.1, involving Morrison shelters were those of the 3rd/4th May, 1941, that is only four months after the prototype had been shown to Mr. Churchill. This reflects a remarkable achievement in the development and nationwide despatch of a mass produced article; the result of team work that, to our discredit, only seems possible in war-time. However, the first full report to reach the Research and Experiments Department was that of the incident, Case 16, which occurred at 2.30 in the morning of 14th June, 1941 when a 50 kg bomb fell on a two-storey terrace house in Portsmouth. I look back to the reading of this report as one of my greatest thrills. It must be remembered that though the underlying principles were straightforward, they were new and the detail design had called for many decisions in an entirely unexplored field. Painful compromise had been faced, particularly in the design of the mattress, and there had been no long term testing programme which would have been considered essential for any peace-time product before a mass-production order covering half a million units had been undertaken.

The order having left our hands we depended thereafter on the efficiency of our supply organisation. The millions of items had to be ordered from the steel industry and delivered to thousands of small workshops all over the country for fabrication. The 359 individual parts of each shelter had then to be collected together and delivered to the householder who, we hoped, would find the handbook we had written, *How to put up your Morrison shelter*, perfectly clear so that, with his Boy Scout helpers, he could produce the complete finished article exactly as we had designed it to be.

I considered, perhaps a little prematurely, that this Portsmouth incident proved beyond doubt the success of the shelter. In the first place, while it had been designed to protect only against a near miss, here was the case of a direct hit. The small bomb had penetrated the roof and had exploded on the first floor completely demolishing the terraced house in which the Morrison shelter had been installed in the living room at the front on the ground floor. The bedroom floor had not hinged about one edge but, while remaining intact and horizontal, had been forced down directly on to the shelter, as can be seen in Fig. 7.1. The main structure had distorted a little as it had, of course, been designed to do. In this incident the debris load was greater than usual because the floor above the shelter had been used as a store and was stacked full of furniture. The end weld-mesh panels or screens had been bent inward by the debris, again as they had been designed to do, and the lath mattress had held in spite of being forced through the floor. The occupants, an old lady, as I first described her when the Morrison shelter was used as a design example in my university lectures, and her dog were released in the space of half an hour uninjured. In the course of time I naturally stopped describing her as "old", in fact she was only 62 years of age, but whatever her age if I could have found the time to travel down to Portsmouth in

TABLE 7.1

Fate of occupants of Morrison shelters in houses badly damaged by near-misses or direct hits from small bombs.

	Case No.	Number of occupants in shelter	Casualties		
			Killed	Seriously injured	Lightly injured
Section A	10(a)	3	0	2	0
Houses completely	10(b)	3 + dog	0	0	0
demolished	16	1 + dog	0	0	0
	17	4	0	0	4
	24	2	0	0	0
	28	4	0	0	1
	30	2	0	0	0
	31	2	0	0	0
	32	5	0	0	0
	35	2	0	0	2
	38	2	0	0	0
	39	4	0	0	0
	40	3	0	0	0
	41	5	0	0	0
	42	3	0	0	2
	43	4	0	0	0
	44	3	2	1	0
	45	1	0	0	0
	46	3	0	0	2
	47	5	1	4	0
	48	1	0	0	1
	50	6	0	0	0
	51	2	0	0	0
	52	5	0	2	0
	53	5	0	0	0
	54	6	0	0	0
	56	4	0	0	0
	57	4	0	1	2
	58	1	0	1	0
	59	1	0	0	0
	60	3	0	0	0
	62	4	0	0	1
	71(b)	3	0	0	0
	71(c)	2	0	1	1
	72	4	0	0	0
	73(b)	3	0	0	0
	73(c)	3	0	0	0
	77	1	0	0	0
Section B	33	4	0	1	0
Houses damaged	36	2	0	0	0
beyond repair	63	5	0	0	0
	80	1	0	0	0
Section C	13	2	0	0	0
Houses damaged so	23	3	0	0	0
as to be uninhabitable					
	Total	136	3	13	16

Fig. 7.1

those hectic June days of 1941 I would have warmly embraced her as the first proof of the efficacy of the shelter.

Had I known it, the first incidents which had occurred in Bootle during the night of the 3rd/4th May were more spectacular and revealing. Here two shelters had been involved and one was also technically a direct hit from a 50 kg bomb, as can be seen from the plan of the two terrace houses in which shelters had been installed in the ground floor back rooms (Fig. 7.2). The houses had been built in 1905 with 9 inch brick walls, ground floors boarding on joists over sleeper walls, first floors boarding on 7 inch by 2 inch joists at 14 inch centres spanning from back to front, parallel to the party wall. The bomb exploded in the back of the front room, that is on a level with the shelter. The houses collapsed. Shelter 1 was pushed through the floor on to the surface concrete 18 inches below. The main frame was severely distorted as one would expect from a hit so direct that one member of the shelter frame was actually penetrated by bomb fragments. There were signs that the flow of debris had been so violent that parts of the weld-mesh screens had pulled away from their retaining bolts. Even more crucial was the behaviour of the mattress. While the laths were recovered intact all the fastening hooks were missing and while six spring hooks were found out of the eighteen, five of them were extended almost to their full length. In fact, in this first and severe test in which the shelter had been forced right through the floor,

SHELTER. 1.

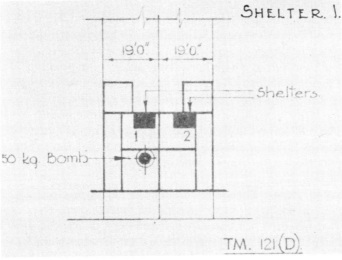

Fig. 7.2

boards and joists, onto the foundations below, the mattress had failed technically but it had held together long enough to protect the occupants. It had proved itself, therefore, to be an optimum design just doing its job and no more as was proved again and again in other later incidents. While highly satisfactory, it must be emphasised that this was pure chance since, as will be recalled, the detailed design was dictated entirely by the material available and the transport difficulties. The three occupants, a woman of 74, a boy of 4 and a girl of 3, were rescued in $1\frac{1}{2}$ hours through the end of the shelter, as shown in Fig. 7.2. The woman had a lacerated arm, the boy facial injuries and the girl suffered from shock. It is sad to relate that two others, possibly the children's parents, who were in the house but had not gone to the shelter, were killed. In shelter 2 were three people and their setter dog. They escaped unhurt, uninjured and unaided.

Another incident, Case 17, was a direct hit on a two-storey brick house in South Shields at 22.56 hours on the night of 8th December, 1941, which caused total collapse of roof, walls and floors. The 250 kg bomb exploded about 16 feet from the shelter which was forced through the floor, but in this case the mattress fixings held, as did the side panels or curtains and the main frame was not seriously distorted. No debris entered the shelter and the four occupants, two women, a man and a child, were uninjured apart from slight abrasions received in their rescue which took place in the near-record time of 10 minutes, no doubt accelerated by the unusual occurrence of fire in the debris.

A large mine exploding in the early evening of 23rd December, 1941 involved no less than five Morrison shelters in an incident at Herne Bay, Cases 18–22. The damage to the houses and to the shelters was caused by the clay thrown out of the large crater 80 feet in diameter and 35 feet deep. The chunks of clay were lethal enough to cause collapse of roofs, floors and chimney breasts; one piece was violent enough to deform the top plate and angle of a shelter by 5 inches, giving one shelterer, who was unfortunate enough to be sitting up at the time, slight concussion. In all, 18 shelterers escaped unaided from these shelters, unhurt except for one other slight injury caused by the ricochet of debris into a shelter, the side screens of which had foolishly not been fitted.

Another multiple incident involving three shelters was also produced by a parachute mine falling at Whitstable at 8.20 in the evening of the 12th October, 1941 producing a crater 70 feet in diameter and 30 feet deep. This mine exploded 50 feet from a row of houses in Victoria Street. They all collapsed, Cases 30–32. The first shelter contained Mrs. Rigden and her daughter. At the time of the incident Mr. Rigden was entering the shelter; he had got his head and shoulders in but his body was weighed down by debris. When the rescuers dug out the family they found the shelter had been blown about 15 feet from its original position. The frame was slightly distorted. No debris had entered the shelter. The report states that Mrs. Rigden and her daughter suffered "no discomfort"; Mr. Rigden was, of course, injured and was taken to hospital. He died a few days later.

In the second shelter at 14 Victoria Street were two women. The shelter was undamaged. Though there was much dust no debris penetrated into the shelter and the occupants reported that after the first shock they had a great feeling of security, largely because they could move about in the shelter. They were fortunate in having an electric torch with them. The third shelter was occupied by a mother and her four children. Their experience could have been very different. Their shelter was called upon to absorb a great deal of energy as can be gathered from the state it was in when dug out of the debris, as shown in Fig. 7.3. This shows what could be considered copy-book behaviour but for the absence of the inner bolt at the top of the right leg. This may have sheared through but it is much

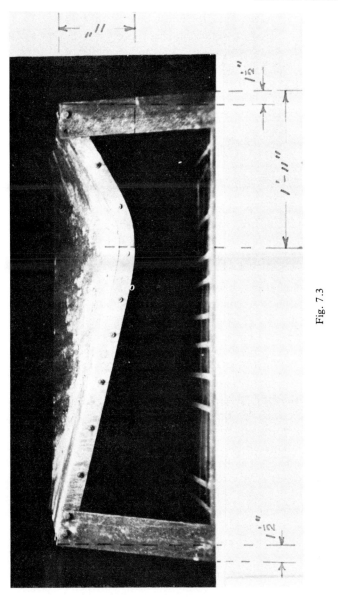

Fig. 7.3

more likely never to have been in place before the incident occurred. Nevertheless, the shelter had behaved as it was designed to do. Not surprisingly the children had at first been frightened at the shock and the idea of being trapped. They had no torch but as there was no debris in the shelter they were soon relieved to be able to feel one another and to crawl about. They were eventually dug out uninjured.

Though the Morrison had been designed for use in a two-storey brick villa type of house it was inevitably used in larger houses where the debris loads were potentially heavier. It successfully coped with these conditions as in the Falmouth incident of 25th November,

1941, Case 28, involving a two-storey house built in 1886 with 20 inch thick stone walls. The shelter was occupied by a woman and her three children when a 250kg bomb dropped just 17 feet from the house which was completely demolished. The shelter was eventually found to be displaced 3 feet and to have dropped 18 inches through the floor. It was even more distorted than that of Fig. 7.3, not only was there a central deflection of about 12 inches of one top angle, but the whole frame had been racked laterally 6 inches by a horizontal force emphasising the value of the rigid joints at all corners. This shelter must have been at about its limit of endurance. Nevertheless the occupants were dug out after 30 minutes' effort uninjured except for the mother's bruised shoulder.

An incident, Case 39, in Weymouth at 10.17 in the evening of 2nd April, 1942 would have had a happier ending if a two-tier Morrison had been issued to the household. A large 1000 kg bomb landed on one side of a street opposite a three-storey semi-detached house in which, in a ground floor front room was a standard shelter. The two floors and the roof all collapsed. The first floor, boarding on 9 inch by 2 inch joists, fell so that one edge rested partly on the ground and partly on the shelter, which it moved 4 feet but scarcely distorted. The shelterers were released unhurt within half an hour. The report states that "the occupants of the shelter were a woman who was very fat and her three children. There was no room in the shelter for the father who sheltered under the stairs and was killed." Three minutes before, in a neighbouring street, an almost identical incident, Case 40, had occurred to a two-storey house. Nevertheless, the depth of the debris, which had been successfully kept out of the shelter by the weld-mesh side curtains, was such that rescue was difficult and the three occupants, though unhurt, were not dug out for more than an hour. In many cases, for instance in two out of three, Cases 41–43, occurring in York on the night of 28/29th April, 1942 though the houses containing the shelters were completely demolished, the occupants, three in one case and four in another, escaped unaided by removing the side curtains.

Many more accounts of lives saved in these indoor shelters could be given as will be gathered from Table 7.1 which lists those incidents reported to the Research and Experiments Department up to May 1943 where rescues were made from demolished or heavily damaged houses.

Unfortunately some deaths did occur in Morrison shelters. Two of these were in an incident, Case 44, at Dover in the early hours of 3rd April, 1942. Strictly speaking a Morrison shelter should not have been issued for this Dover house since it was too high and heavy, having three storeys and an attic built of 14 inch thick brick walls up to first floor and 9 inches above. The ground floor consisted of 1 inch boarding on 4 inch by 3 inch joists over sleeper walls. The house was completely demolished by a very near miss from a 500 kg bomb. The shelter was slewed around through an angle of 75 degrees displaced 4 feet 6 inches and forced 18 inches through the floor. The floor joists appear to have broken, possibly over a sleeper wall. The bottom longitudinal members of the shelter were deflected upwards 12 inches, probably by being bent across the sleeper wall. All the mattress fittings had failed and floor joists and boards had penetrated through the bottom of the shelter to within 18 inches of the top. There were three occupants. It took the rescuers $10\frac{1}{2}$ hours to dig down to them. They found one alive, but severely injured and the other two dead from asphyxiation. The height of the house and therefore the amount of debris was excessive, but it is possible that had the mattress fittings been stronger as they had been originally designed and were in the two-tier version all three occupants of this shelter might have survived. It is interesting to note that after recovery new longitudinal and mattress members were fitted and this shelter was re-issued for further use.

In an incident, Cases 46 and 47, at Ipswich in the early morning of 2nd June, 1942, two Morrison shelters were involved, one with three occupants in a bungalow, No. 125 Bexley Road, and the other with five occupants in a two-storey semi-detached house, No. 129. The position of the shelters before and after the incident and of the bombs and craters are shown in Fig. 7.4. A 500 kg bomb fell 65 feet from the corner of the bungalow which was demolished, burying the shelter in debris. A second bomb, almost immediately afterwards, was a direct hit on the corner of the room containing the shelter which was blown 10

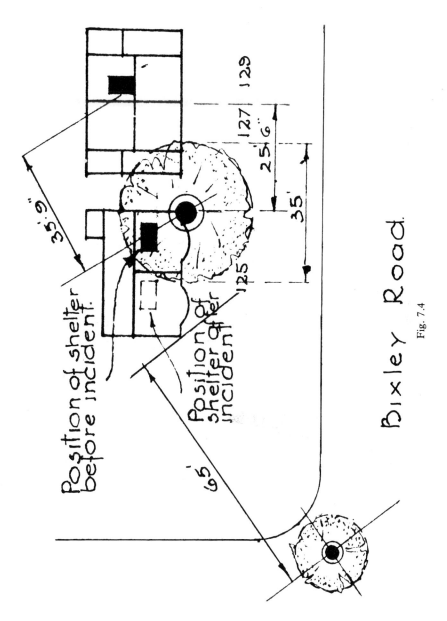

Fig. 7.4

feet into the next room, to some extent freeing it from debris since the occupants escaped unaided. Though the other shelter in the house, No. 129, was 35 feet 9 inches further away from the bomb its occupants were not so fortunate. They were a father, mother and three young people and they have provided personal accounts of what happened. They were awakened by gunfire a little before 2 o'clock in the morning. They dressed and went to the shelter, though two of the young people remained for a few minutes watching a fire which had broken out on the heath nearby. The father left the house to go on fire-watch duty. The back door was locked and the front door slammed behind him, preventing his return. An incendiary bomb fell close to the house and started a fire which the father extinguished. Blast from a bomb some distance away blew down the back door and enabled the father to enter the house and join his family in the Morrison shelter. Oil bombs and high explosives were falling, two in quick succession. The house was demolished and the shelter, undamaged, was completely buried and the occupants, though unhurt, could not make their way out. The heath fires spread to the debris. The Fire Brigade arrived and played water on the fire while the rescue party dug through the debris. The rescue took between two and three hours, by which time the shelterers were so badly scalded from the water played onto the burning building and trickling on them that they had to be taken to hospital, where the 45-year-old mother eventually died from shock caused by her burns. This is the only recorded case of a fatality from fire in a Morrison incident, a risk which, it will be remembered, figured very largely in the minds of the panel of engineers responsible for Command Paper 5932. It should be noted that there were no recorded casualties from coal-gas poisoning.

A fatal incident, occurring in Yarmouth at 2.30 in the morning of 30th May, 1942, Case 49, was not as clearly reported as it might have been. Apparently a 500 kg bomb made a direct hit on a pair of semi-detached houses Nos. 1 and 2 Albany Road, in each of which was a Morrison shelter containing one occupant. The bomb demolished both houses. The shelter in No. 2 must have been near the centre of the explosion, virtually a direct hit, since it was blown on to the debris of No. 1. The frame was distorted. One longitudinal bottom angle was missing altogether, and a side bottom angle was severely twisted. All side screens and the mattress were missing. The occupant died due to shock and suffocation. The report does not say where his body was found or whether it was buried in the debris. The occupant of No. 1, Case 48, fared better since he was involved in what technically could be described as a "near-miss" incident. His shelter remained completely intact apart from the failure of a few mattress fixings. However, it took the rescuers three hours to dig him out; he was only lightly injured.

Another even more remarkable incident involving two shelters took place in Exeter at 1.45 in the morning of 4th May, 1942. There was one shelter in No. 176 of a two-storey terrace and another in No. 180. According to the report a 250 kg bomb exploded on the house between, No. 178, producing a crater 34 feet in diameter and 12 feet deep. This entirely engulfed No. 178 and most of the adjoining houses. The shelter in No. 180, Case 55, must have been well within the crater area since, with its three occupants, an adult and two children, still inside, it was blown clean out of the house from the position shown by a cross in Fig. 7.5 over a communal shelter, that is a surface shelter 10 feet high which can be seen in the street outside, right across the street coming to rest after a flight of 46 feet in the first floor room of a house opposite, shown by the circled cross in Fig. 7.5. One child was only slightly injured, but the other child and the adult were taken to hospital where the child subsequently died. The shelter in No. 176, Case 56, was treated slightly less

Fig. 7.5

violently. It was blown 6 feet away and landed 5 feet up on the debris of the house. It was undamaged and the four occupants, unhurt, escaped unaided.

In an incident, Case 65, at Birmingham in the early hours of 28th July, 1942 a 1000 kg bomb fell in a row of two-storey terrace houses. Many houses were demolished, including one, four houses away from the bomb, in which was a Morrison shelter. Two people were reported killed. It was an unusual occurrence since the occupants of the house were not dug out of the debris for $11\frac{1}{2}$ hours, when they were found to be dead. The Morrison shelter was almost squashed flat and was first reported as a failure. However 18 of the 32 main bolts were missing together with one of the main angle members and it later transpired that the shelter had never been erected.

There were inevitably cases in which the bomb exploded in or on the shelter, a direct hit against which nothing could give protection. One such, Case 70, occurred at Eastbourne at 1 o'clock in the morning of 26th October, 1942. Three very small adjoining two-storey terrace houses, with frontages of only 13 feet, contained Morrison shelters. At the time of the incident that in No. 1 had four occupants, that in No. 2 two occupants, while No. 3 was empty. Unfortunately a 500 kg bomb fell right on the No. 1 shelter, blowing it to pieces, only small fragments being found among the wreckage. All four occupants were killed instantly. Shelter No. 2, which was in the crater area, was blown into the next door house No. 3, with the main frame badly damaged and side curtains missing, so that there was a strong assumption that they had never been fitted. The shelter was buried under debris, from which the occupants were dug in one hour. One was dead but the other was only lightly injured. A somewhat similar incident, Case 71, occurred at Tynemouth just after midnight on 3rd November, 1942 when a 500 kg bomb fell on a group of five three-storey houses containing Morrison shelters. That in No. 15 had five occupants, No. 13 had two and No. 8 had three. Unfortunately the bomb exploded in the shelter at No. 15 blowing it to pieces, the top plate being picked up 50 feet away. There were no survivors. No. 13 was demolished, its shelter was thrown across the room but the occupants survived and were rescued in 20 minutes, one seriously injured and the other lightly injured. The occupants of No. 8, which also was demolished, escaped unaided and uninjured.

These events were almost exactly repeated, Case 73, at 2.30 in the morning of 10th January, 1943 in the same town, when a 500 kg bomb fell on three adjacent two-storey terrace houses, choosing unerringly the shelter with the most occupants. The shelter was blown 30 feet away, badly damaged and holed by fragments, with all its occupants killed. The shelters in the other two houses, which were demolished, each had three occupants, one group was rescued unhurt in 40 minutes and the others escaped unhurt and unaided.

While in many of the cases where occupants were injured by debris there was a strong suspicion that they had not fixed the weld-mesh side screens after getting into the shelter, there were surprisingly few cases of disaster because the shelter had been wrongly placed in the room. One such occurred at Hastings on 9th February, 1943, Case 75. The shelter was in a normal two-storey brick semi-detached house. It had been placed, without any regard to the instructions for the need of lateral protection, in line with the front door of the house, the door to the room and a French window. A bomb exploded across the street 22 feet from the house and more than 40 feet from the shelter. The house did not collapse but fragments of the bomb entered through the front door, the door of the room and into the shelter, where they killed two of the occupants and seriously injured the third.

It is impossible to protect some people from themselves, as was shown by the pathetic case of the Morrison shelter erected under a timber trailer caravan standing in a yard at

Norwich, Case 61. On 29th April, 1942 a large bomb fell 35 feet from the shelter. It was blown to smithereens, while the four occupants died from multiple injuries.

At Lowestoft a pathetic incident, Case 45, occurred at 1.20 in the morning of 5th June, 1942. A 500 kg bomb fell 20 feet from the corner of a bungalow, 23 feet from a Morrison shelter in the back room. The crater was 48 feet in diameter and 12 feet deep so that the shelter was actually in the crater area. The bungalow, inevitably, was demolished. There was only one occupant of the shelter, a child, who escaped unaided. When seen by the rescue squad she was crossing the debris to get assistance for her parents, who were subsequently found dead in their bedroom. It had been their habit to go themselves to the shelter only when an "alert" sounded. In this case the bomb fell before the "alert".

Table 7.1 gives particulars of the casualties in 44 typical incidents involving heavy damage to houses, reported before the end of May 1943. This was virtually before the flying bomb (V1) epidemic in which the shelter was again very much involved. The Table is divided into three. Section A refers to shelters in houses which were completely demolished, Section B to houses damaged beyond repair and Section C to houses so damaged as to be uninhabitable. Table 7.2 lists shelters which were improperly erected or which suffered direct hits. In the categories A, B and C of Table 7.1 out of a grand total of 136 occupants there were only three fatal casualties with 13 seriously injured and 16 lightly injured, the latter sustaining nothing more than slight abrasions usually received during rescue.

The success of a shelter is not only measured by the reduction in casualties, quite as important is the comfort and peace of mind of the millions who used it every night and, on occasion, during the day-time. An interesting testimonial is given by Norman Longmate in his fascinating history of everyday life duing the War[1] when he says ". . . the Morrison proved the most successful shelter of the war, particularly during the 'hit and

TABLE 7.2

Other Casualties

Case No.	Number in shelter	Casualties		
		killed	Seriously injured	Lightly injured
49[1]	1	1	0	0
55[1]	3	1	1	1
61[2]	4	4	0	0
65[3]	2	2	0	0
70(a)[1]	4	4	0	0
70(b)[1]	2	1	0	1
71(a)[1]	5	5	0	0
73(a)[1]	4	4	0	0
75[4]	3	2	1	0

(1) Direct hit on shelter
(2) Shelter erected under timber caravan
(3) Shelter had not been erected
(4) Shelter wrongly sited—casualties due to bomb fragments.

[1] Norman Longmate, *How We Lived Then*, Hutchinson & Co. Ltd., London, 1971.

run' and flying-bomb raids when a family had only a few seconds to get under cover. It was also a good deal easier to erect than an Anderson, and while most people remember their nights in the Anderson with horror, memories of the Morrison shelter are usually good-humoured.''

CHAPTER 8

Other Shelters

Though the Civil Defence Research Committee was to prove an ineffectual instrument for innovation, it set out with the best of practical intentions. At its second meeting on Friday, 19th May, 1939 a sub-committee "B" was set up consisting of Southwell, Pippard, Thomas and myself with terms of reference "to consider design methods for structural air raid protection". Much of the first meeting of the sub-committee on 26th May was taken up with a consideration of the design of bomb-proof shelters, but Stradling also brought forward the subject of debris loads as recommended by the Home Office, to be assumed in the design of strutting for basement shelters. To check the Home Office recommendations a series of tests had been carried out by collapsing houses on to basements strengthened with the standard tubular strutting mentioned in Chapter 5. Although high impact factors were measured the standard strutting had not collapsed. The following exchange, as recorded in the Minutes, then took place. It is of interest in the light of later events.

"Professor Baker stated that he would like to see some provision, e.g. bracing, for laterial stability. Dr. Thomas of the Building Research Station, replied that in the later tests the steel joists had been taken to the walls to provide for this."

Thomas' statement apparently satisfied me. It should not have done so. My instinctive feeling about the need for lateral stability was sound, but I was not far-sighted enough to foresee the knock-on effect through the walls which was to cause so many casualties eighteen months later. The Committee asked me to prepare a short note on basement strengthening.

At the fourth meeting on 11th July, 1939 this note was presented. The Home Office recommendations stated that the effect of a falling building should be represented by an equivalent static debris load varying from 200 lb per square foot of floor for a framed building to 400 lb per square foot for a five or more storey load bearing building, that is one with the floors supported by walls of brick or masonry. The engineer was to design the strengthening structure in the basement to support this "equivalent" load, using his normal simplified design formulae and working stresses (e.g. 8 tons per square inch for steel), just as he had designed the original building to support floor loads, sometimes called super-load, the intensities of which were laid down in the city's Building Code.

I explained that it was misleading to compare the loads in the recommendations with those in the Building Code. In dealing with the original peace-time building the designer, by the use of his low working stresses produced a structure which had a "factor of safety", that is one capable without collapse or the growth of large deflections of supporting loads greater than those specified. This factor was to cover such misfortunes as accidental overload. I expressed the opinion that there was no necessity to introduce the same factor into the design of basement strengthening since the debris load was in the nature of an accidental overload. I then drew on my recently acquired knowledge of the collapse of beams from my Bristol research to demonstrate that the Home Office loads were adequate, as in fact the experience of bombing was to bear out.

At the same meeting there was particular discussion of basements in fully framed, i.e. skyscraper type, buildings. I was asked to discuss the matter with Mr. W. L. Scott, a consulting engineer and the leading authority in London on the design of reinforced concrete structures.

The discussion took place on the morning of 21st July before the fifth meeting, which Mr. Scott attended. Dr. Stradling reported on the discussion and said that "Professor Baker and Mr. Scott had been able to give valuable help on the practical aspects involved in regard to steel framed and reinforced concrete buildings respectively".

The Minutes of the meeting continued:

"Professor Baker thought that a rule could be drawn up such as that which he had suggested at the morning discussion, namely that where in a fully framed structure the floor was, in fact, only carrying a quarter of the super-load for which it was designed, then no strengthening was required. Mr. Scott stated that there were many cases, especially in entrance halls, where a floor designed to carry 80 lb per square foot or more super-load, was actually carrying only 20 lb per square foot.

"It was finally agreed that the recommendations to be satisfied by a structure in order that it should not require strengthening should be as follows: (1) the building should be fully framed, (2) the floor over the basement should be designed for a minimum super-load of 80 lb per square foot, (3) the floor should be actually carrying a super-load not more than one quarter of its designed super-load, (4) cases where heavy machinery is situated on upper floors above the basement should receive special consideration."

This recommendation from the Research Committee was passed on to the Local Authorities with commendable speed by the administrative branch in a document entitled "Factors which should be taken into account in selecting buildings for shelter under emergency conditions", attached to a letter from the Home Office Air Raid Precautions Department dated 28th August, 1939 headed "ARP Department Circular No. 204/1939".

My interest in basement strengthening continued. The obvious and simplest step to take in strengthening a floor was to insert a prop under each floor joist at its centre of length but according to the Home Office recommendations this would, at the best, only allow a small additional equivalent static load to be carried. In some cases it would allow none at all. This can be appreciated if one considers a floor over a basement supported on steel joists having built-in ends as shown in Fig. 4.6(a). If, for instance, the joists had been carrying their full design load, under which the permissible working stress of 8 tons per square inch was developed at the end sections where the large hogging bending moments occur, before the prop was inserted then no matter how small the equivalent static load added to the propped beam the permissible working stress would be exceeded at the ends, since additional hogging-bending moments would be introduced there. According to the code, therefore, and to the elastic method of design which it postulated, the propping would provide no strengthening. In fact, of course, the propped joist could carry without collapse many times the load intensity for which it had originally been designed. By using the arguments presented in Chapter 4 it was possible to show that the propped beam could carry a load nearly eleven times that for which the original beam was designed. Propping, therefore, produced considerable strengthening of the joist and, incidentally, the result was independent of any reasonable sinking of the prop under load. It was, therefore, independent of the amount of load carried by the joist before the prop was inserted.

All this, with simple rules to guide the designer, was set out at some length since it was the first practical application of the new plastic method of structural design, in Bulletin No. Cl, the first of a new series published by the Research and Experiments Department. Its title was *New Design Methods for Strutting of Basements*. Structural engineers will be interested to know that it was when working on this problem that I discovered the phenomenon of the moving plastic hinge.

The design rules appeared simultaneously as "Ministry of Home Security Chief Engineer's Branch Circular CE/General/33" and was signed "F. Webster A/CE 9th April, 1940". This was a remarkable example of co-operation and trust between a research department and the executive authority because the design rules embodied in this Circular CE/General/33 were based on a concept so new that the engineers, including Webster, Rouse's deputy in the Chief Engineer's Branch, could not have been familiar with it. How did this goodwill and ready collaboration between the Research and Experiments Department and the Chief Engineer's Branch come to evaporate so sadly and almost disastrously before Mr. Morrison's visit to Princes Risborough in October 1940?

Could it have been the appearance of an article in the April 1940 issue of a technical journal *Architectural Design and Construction*, entitled

A.R.P. STRENGTHENING OF STRUCTURES FOR AIR ATTACK
(Important Statement from Ministry of Home Security, A.R.P. Department)
By Professor J.F. BAKER, M.A., Sc.D., D.Sc., Assoc. M. Inst. C.E., M.I. Struct. E., of the Research and Experiments Branch, Ministry of Home Security, A.R.P. Dept.

together with a similar article in the October 1940 issue of the *Journal of the Institution of Civil Engineers*. Though I had never been averse at any time to legitimate publicity for my work I could not in wartime have submitted for publication these articles myself. They must have gone officially from the Research and Experiments Branch and with Stradling's blessing. This puff for the Branch may well have irritated Rouse. One can imagine him taking up the matter with Stradling. No doubt by October a *modus vivendi*, or a dividing of the spoils or spheres of influence between the two principals, had been arranged but, if so, it was done without any explanation to their junior colleagues—I certainly knew nothing about it.

However irritating my articles may have been they were far-sighted contributions. They were written before there was any bomb damage, yet they tell with uncanny accuracy what would occur and what steps could be taken to minimise damage. They deal in the first place with the multi-storey frame building, mentioned above, and then continue with the single-storey modern steel factory building which will be dealt with in a later chapter. They are, of course, based on my realisation of the importance of plastic behaviour arising from the Bristol tests. They contain such statements as:

"It may be said that wherever continuity can be introduced it is desirable" and "An examination of the real strength of the structure must be made. It should be remembered, for instance, that failure does not necessarily take place when the yield stress of the material is developed at one section", but nowhere is any hint given of the absorption of energy due to this continuity and ductility. There is no doubt that the full realisation of this came only later at the interview with Morrison.

The forecasts were completely justified by events when the bombs fell. Older types of buildings which were not fully framed had walls which were load bearing. These walls were not ductile so they were liable to collapse when subjected to a near miss, as did the walls of the houses containing Morrison shelters and of the early unreinforced brick shelters, bringing down with them the floors and roof they had originally supported. They were also liable to downward spreading collapse as was illustrated by the incident at Queen Anne's Mansions, the great brick built block of Victorian flats in Westminster. A small bomb exploded on the top floor which collapsed onto the one below, the weight of debris caused this also to collapse and so on through the full seven storeys.

Steel framed buildings were almost impervious to near misses even when they were most damaging as in the case of the block of flats in Westminster Gardens, London. Here a large 1000 kg bomb fell under the corner of the building cutting through the corner steel stanchion and the one next to it; though these two members were continuous to the top of the building and so played a part, in peaceful times, in supporting each of the ten floors, no collapse occurred. Since the members cut were not symmetrically placed in the building there was some settlement at the damaged corner and twisting of the whole building took place, one top corner moving horizontally 13 inches. This was shown in a most interesting way up the height of the building. The timber floor boards in each storey, opened up until in the top-most flat, the gap between the boards was 13 inches wide.

Very little damage occurred even when there was a direct hit from a medium size bomb, so that the amendment to the recommendations suggested for basement strengthening proved quite conservative. While it was usual for approximately 1000 square feet of fire resisting floor above and below the explosion to be demolished, the area of demolition fell off rapidly to about 100 square feet and the debris was usually held by the second or third floor slab below the explosion.

While reinforced concrete framed buildings behaved somewhat differently from those of steel there was no measurable difference in the damage to floors.

I took my confidence and enthusiasm for shelter in framed buildings to the Shelter Policy Committee. I prepared for it a document "Provision of Air Raid Shelters in Framed Buildings" dated 12th October, 1940. The summary provided read as follows:

(1) Recent experience has shown the inherent resistance of fully framed structures to air raid damage.

(2) When a bomb hits an old time wall bearing structure the walls and floor in the immediate neighbourhood of the explosion are brought down and the resulting debris falling on the floor below is often sufficient to demolish it and so on down to the basement.

(3) In a fully framed building, however, it is almost impossible to cause damage which will give rise to serious debris loads. Structural damage is confined to the floor and bay in which the bomb explodes.

(4) A large number of bombs have scored direct hits on multi-storey buildings with fire resisting floors. In none of these cases has the bomb penetrated more than the roof and three floors.

(5) The worst damage from near misses occurs in the ground floor of the building; on the middle floors the damage is small.

(6) On the middle floors of fully framed buildings with fire resisting floors as they stand today the protection provided is good, rather better than in the normal above ground brick shelter.

(7) Where on the middle floor of fully framed buildings overhead cover is provided by at least the roof and four floors of fire resisting construction, if the internal partitions are

removed, ceilings stripped of plaster and window openings bricked up to a height of 6 feet, a much higher degree of protection is provided.

(8) The value of the basements in framed buildings has already been recognised, the degree of protection in them can be greatly increased by building a heavy reinforced concrete wall to cut off the area under the pavement from the basement proper.

This document received a warm welcome from Miss Wilkinson. She shared with me the picture of thousands of London families from the East End streaming in each evening to the City and West End to occupy those almost bomb-proof areas of the multi-storey framed office blocks. The wires began to hum. There is a Minute dated 21st October, 1940 from me to Mr. Welch, an efficient and helpful administrative officer who acted as Stradling's personal assistant. It says:

"I had a telephone conversation with Miss Macower from the Cabinet Office asking if we needed more information about the accommodation in framed buildings in London. This arises out of the proposal to use such buildings as air raid shelters.

"I had telephoned the LCC earlier in the week and have been informed that there were 4000 such buildings and that it would mean heavy labour to obtain more information such as floor area of each building, number of storeys, whether fire-proof floors and the position of the buildings.

"At the time I made the enquiry the question of using these buildings had not been presented officially but in view of the drive which is likely to be made now I think it is time that more active steps were taken. Could you find from the Chief Engineer's Department whether he has done anything in this and if not what he thinks should be done?"

However the drive did not develop. Very little shelter space for the public became available. It was not a case of the socialist Minister being taught some of the facts of life by the property owners and being warned off their premises. This certainly did not occur. Miss Wilkinson must have used all her authority for there is a letter signed by Sir George Gater to all principal officers dated 11th November, 1940 and headed "Steel Framed Buildings". It reads:

"At the meeting with the Regional Commissioners on 25th October the Minister spoke of the question of utilising the protection available in steel framed buildings including the first and second floors, that is where those have four floors plus a roof above them. The question of using such buildings where they are available for shelter has been of special prominence in London where the number of such buildings is large and the need for increased dormitory shelter great and after discussion between the Department and the Regional Commissioner a Circular, a copy of which is enclosed, was issued to Local Authorities in the London region with, it will be observed, special reference to Central London."

With Gater's letter went one from Harold Scott, then Chief Administrative Officer of the London Civil Defence Region. It was dated 24th October, 1940 and headed "Dormitory Shelter in Central London". The first two paragraphs point out the value of unstrutted basements in fully framed buildings. The third paragraph deals with the provision of additional shelter which, it is claimed, is being hampered by an obstructive attitude on the part of some occupiers of suitable premises. It goes on:

"Some business houses, for instance, want to retain an excessive amount of space as dormitories for employees or for carrying on of businesses curtailed by the war. Some owners of flats refused to anyone but their tenants access to basement shelter far greater than their need. It is, of course, very proper that business concerns which must remain in

London should make arrangements for staff to sleep there during the present traffic difficulties and this must be recognised as a first charge on their space but the provision so made must be no more than is reasonably necessary for the number of people who are to be accommodated. Its restriction to that standard and the release for public shelter of what is superfluous must be vigorously pressed and, if necessary, enforced. In carrying out this policy the upper floors, as defined above, of fully framed buildings must be regarded as giving as suitable shelter as basements, whether for the public or for the staff. Similarly claims that spaces wanted for the carrying on of business should be scrutinised no less searchingly than claims that it is needed for staff dormitories and the availability of the space for shelter should not be regarded as ruled out merely by the fact that taking it may disturb to some extent the existing arrangements for carrying on the business which could do with less space."

There is a sad little memorandum in my handwriting at the end of my personal file A1/13 "Shelter and Protection in Framed Buildings". It reads:

"The obvious superiority of the framed building over all other types makes it difficult at this time to acquire space for shelter since the present occupants and owners are fully aware of their good fortune. Many steel skeletons exist, however, in London and the larger provincial towns, the frameworks of buildings under construction when the war began. These masses of steel at present of no value to the community could be made into invaluable highly protected shelter at the expenditure of a certain amount of cement, which is at present in good supply, and of very little additional steel in the form of bars for reinforcing floors. The upper floors which would not be used as shelter would be available as fire-proof space which is at a premium in all cities."

There is no evidence that this suggestion ever saw the light of day.

In spite of the poor response to the plea for space in multi-storey framed buildings it is interesting to note that Miss Wilkinson was still consulting me in March 1941 about similar proposals. A Minute to her dated 10th March, 1941 says:

"Mr. Arup's construction is interesting and appears to us to be a real contribution to the problem. This suggestion is the same in principle to that we made in October last for the use of framed buildings as shelters. There is something to be said for Mr. Arup's construction (solid walls instead of stanchions and panel walls), so long as the design is such that secondary collapse does not result from the destruction of a load bearing wall. . . ."

The last mention of shelter in framed buildings occurs in a Minute from me to Stradling of 18th October, 1941 accompanying the final draft of a new document "Handbook of Air Raid Shelter Design" and signals another minor difference of opinion with the Chief Engineer.

"You will see that I have reduced it to about three-quarters of the length of the original draft, mainly by cutting down the section "Indoor Shelters" which Sir Alexander Rouse thought rather superfluous.

"There is only one point left in the document which you should, I think, take up with Sir Alexander. In Section 6, Provision of Shelter in Framed Buildings, sub-paragraph E, I have stated that since the framed building provides such good protection it is suggested that the number of persons to be accommodated in any one compartment should be limited to 200. On the original draft Sir Alexander had queried this and substituted 50. Whereas 50 persons is the usually accepted limit for the normal type of surface shelter I think that 200 is a satisfactory number in a framed building where the overhead cover is such that the chance of a bomb penetrating to a compartment is reduced very appreciably. There is not, so far as I know, any suggestion to confine the occupants of one compartment in a tunnel shelter to 50 and I do not think there is this necessity in the case of a framed building."

A small number of commercially produced indoor shelters had been available before the war. One, of stout steel construction, had been made by Robert Morris Ltd. of Farnworth, Bolton. There were records of two incidents where it had behaved excellently in the blitz and saved lives. When the Morrison shelter made its appearance early in 1941 a renewed demand arose from householders living in areas which did not qualify for the Government free issue and before Morrisons were available for sale. Commercial interests were soon clamouring for permission to satisfy this demand.

Experience in the development of our own shelter had highlighted some of the dangers inherent in this novel form of structure so it was decided to issue guidance to designers and to set up a station at the Research and Experiments Department where prototype shelters could be tested and certified before being put on the open market.

Bulletin No. C16, "Notes on Indoor (Anti-debris) Shelters", was issued on 25th February 1941. It gave as much guidance as possible to designers, covering much the same ground as Chapter 6 above, and set out the tests to which the shelter would be subjected. The great difficulty was that designers had no knowledge of plastic behaviour or any practical method of designing for energy absorption which was, of course, the crux of the matter. We attempted to help by introducing the device, used before the war for designing basement strengthening as described at the beginning of this chapter, of equivalent static loads. These loads were for an all steel shelter, 200 lb per square foot vertical and 100 lb per square foot horizontal. Three times these intensities were suggested for the less ductile material pre-cast concrete. However the Bulletin's closing words were "Satisfactory resistance to the tests . . . must provide the only ultimate criterion as to the suitability of an indoor shelter".

For the tests the shelter rested at the centre of a one inch thick timber floor supported by brick walls sixteen feet six inches apart and a central sleeper wall eighteen inches thick. In the first test a block of masonry weighing three hundredweight was dropped from a height of six feet on to the top of the shelter; in the second the shelter was given a horizontal blow of intensity 2000 lb-feet from a swinging timber floor and in the third a similar floor weighing 3000 lb swung down from a height of nine feet giving the shelter a vertical blow. With this floor still resting on the shelter additional static load of 400 lb per square foot of shelter area was added representing the weight of the upper walls of the house which might fall on the already collapsed bedroom floor.

A considerable number of commercially designed shelters were tested but very few could be passed as satisfactory. Constructional steel was not available, except for the Morrison shelter, and it was extremely difficult to design anything in reinforced concrete which would stand up to the rigorous conditions and at the same time be light enough to erect in a private house.

However a most successful timber indoor shelter was designed by two members of the staff of the Forest Products Research Laboratory in collaboration with the Design and Development Section. Full instructions for its construction were contained in Bulletin No. C21 published on 22nd August, 1941. A general view is shown in Fig. 8.1; salvage timber from blitzed houses of which twenty shillings worth could be bought per month without a licence, was the recommended material. The overall dimensions were the same

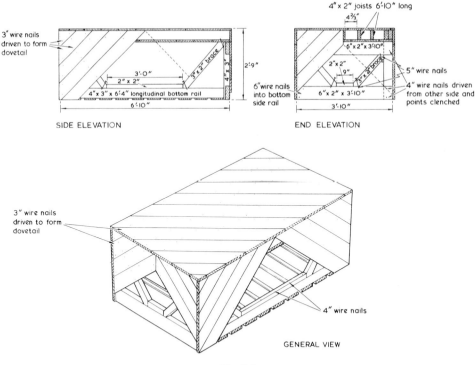

Fig. 8.1

as for the Morrison shelter. The top was made of nine pieces of 4 inch by 2 inch timber laid lengthways to which were nailed top and bottom skins of floor boarding at 45 degrees. The bottom of the shelter consisted of boards nailed to the bottom of two longitudinal members 4 inches by 3 inches. The end frames were 4 inch by 3 inch uprights, 6 inch by 2 inch horizontal members and bracing members with diagonal side boarding on all faces as shown, leaving openings only just big enough for a shelterer to crawl through. The cost of materials including nails and fire retarding paint varied from £3 to £4.10s. according to the timber used, while a skilled craftsman could finish the job in 24 man-hours. This shelter passed the Research and Experiments Department's tests with flying colours. It bounced gaily when the floor fell on it and was not even dented.

By April 1942 the provision of shelters in Britain was so well advanced that the Design and Development Section felt able to give some attention to the needs of other countries. Designs were prepared for more timber shelters and were published as Bulletin C26 "Timber shelters for countries where timber is plentiful and steel difficult to obtain". In it was illustrated, Fig. 8.2, a surface shelter to give about the same protection as the standard reinforced brick shelter. A thickness of 2 feet 6 inches of compact earth in the walls and a minimum of 18 inches on the roof provided the protection from bomb fragments. On suitable sites the shelter could be semi-sunk, thus gaining the advantage of the excavated earth to cover the shelter. The outer boarding retaining the earth would not then be necessary. Main frames were provided at 7 foot centres bolted at the corners and cross-braced with timbers bolted to the frames at the crossing points. Intermediate frames were also bolted at the corners but strengthened only with small corner bracings nailed to the frames. The frames were joined together by two layers of 1 inch boarding, one layer longitudinal and the other at 45 degrees. Three tier bunks were provided, the supports being made integral with the main structure. Entrances were formed by extending two adjacent main frames outwards with suitable screening. An entrance at each end was preferable, otherwise an emergency exit could be provided by a length of large diameter drainpipe filled with earth and fitted with removable covers. As can be seen, the outer boarding retaining the earth fill was not an integral part of the structure but was merely wired to the main frame. It was thus free to disintegrate under the effects of a very near miss without injury to the main structure.

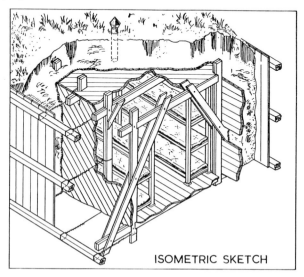

ISOMETRIC SKETCH

Fig. 8.2

This shelter was subjected to what had now become the standard bombing test using a buried 250 kg bomb. The shelter 35 feet long was so built that the bomb was 20 feet away from the mid-point of the long side of the inner wall. Two types "A" and "B" of construction of the main frames were tested. The left hand half "A" had these frames sloping down and outwards as in Fig. 8.2., while in the right half "B" they sloped down, from points outside the shelter on an extended upper horizontal member, inwards where they were connected to the lower horizontal member inside the shelter.

As a result of the explosion the shelter only moved a very small distance. The outer skin on the side nearer the crater broke away over a length of 20 feet and the outer skin on the opposite side fell outwards on the side built with "B" type frames, thus releasing the earth fill over this length. The damage to the rest of the shelter was confined to cracking of a number of the horizontal members in the roof and fracture of two at the centre of length. This damage was discovered to be due to two large pieces of debris weighing 700 and 300 lb respectively which had fallen on the roof. No casualties would have occurred in the shelter and the damage it sustained could have been easily repaired.

Details were also given in the Bulletin of a timber trench lining, of much the same form as the surface shelter, which would have been quite satisfactory against bombs exploding on the surface but would be liable to damage from a bomb exploding in the ground at a distance one and a half times that at which the surface shelter would be undamaged.

A timber indoor shelter designed for construction in empire hardwoods was also detailed. It followed closely the original design of Fig. 8.1 but bolts were used for assembly, as far as possible, the units being designed for prefabrication as standard interchangeable sections easily erected by unskilled labour. The top was laminated and in two sections for ease in handling.

Though, as the war progressed, the policy towards the provision of bomb-proof shelters for the civilian population did not change, the Civil Defence Research Committee, as recorded earlier in this Chapter, had given some consideration to the technical problems of highly resistant structures. Some of these were needed for military purposes and the Design and Development Section advised Mr. B. L. Hurst who was appointed to design, among others, the Admiralty fortress which, now modestly clothed in creeper, still survives on the Horse Guards Parade, London. The most popular shelter which came near to being bomb-proof was, of course, the London tube, or underground railway. No structural additions were needed and so the Design and Development Section was not involved but we did work on other tunnel shelters, a few of which became available for civilian or military purposes. Mr. D. C. Burn was mainly responsible for this work assisted later by a geologist, Captain F. W. Anderson.

CHAPTER 9

Protection of Factories

With shelter design out of the way it is now possible to return to the activity which brought the Design and Development Section, RE4 into being. It will be remembered from Chapter 2 that, looking about for useful occupation in the early days of the phoney-war period, I stumbled on the problem of the factory building and its susceptibility to collapse when damaged by a bomb explosion.

While it is tempting to enlarge on this subject, enough has been said in Chapter 2, where our first contact with Sir Ernest Simon and his team in the North West was described, to define the problem. Moreover, the short technical discussion of Chapter 4 and the subsequent description of shelter design gives the key to the solution. Anyone wanting greater detail or a description of some of the more spectacular war-time collapses should refer to a technical paper written in 1948.[1]

It was fortunate that one of the first factories visited in the North West made the deepest impression. It was an immense building recently erected for the assembly of bomber aircraft with north-light roof trusses, supported by eight rows of great steel apex lattice girders, like young bridges, 30 feet deep, more than 635 feet long placed 65 feet apart. It provided the wide open spaces needed for the erection of large bomber aircraft and would, of course, have supported all the peace-time loads induced by wind and weather. However, in spite of its warlike purpose, no thought had been given to the possible effect of damage due to enemy action. The structure proved to be incredibly vulnerable, so much so that one medium sized bomb dropping anywhere in a considerably "vulnerable area" might easily cause the total collapse of the 350 000 square feet of factory.

Further study showed that all long-span buildings, other than one particular type known popularly as the "umbrella" roof, were susceptible to "spreading collapse". What was perhaps more serious was that a bomb exploding anywhere on one of the shorter span single-storey steel structures comprising the vast majority of industrial buildings, was liable to bring down unnecessarily large areas of the main structure even though the collapse did not spread.

Fortunately in all cases, as my Bristol research indicated, these collapses could be eliminated quite easily and cheaply even in existing steel structures by introducing welded joints, and additional members where spreading collapse was a danger, to ensure continuity in what was already a ductile structure.

When the bombs began to fall in the summer of 1940 what we had foreseen happened. There was devastating spreading collapse and much other structural damage which need not have occurred. I did not wait for this confirmation but went, in October 1939,

[1] Baker, J. F., Leader-Williams, E. and Lax, D., *The Design of Framed Buildings against High-explosive Bombs*, The Civil Engineer in War, Insitution of Civil Engineers, London, 1948.

immediately and directly with my warning to those responsible for the construction and the protection of war factories.

There was a Director-General of Aircraft Factories and also an officer in charge of the ARP, or as it was sometimes called the Passive Air Defence (PAD), of each supply Ministry, that is the Admiralty and the Ministries of Aircraft Production, Supply and Works. All these I approached. My diary for the month of November 1939 is interesting.

"1st November—discussed with Bernal the effect of blast on factory buildings; discussed with Wing Commander Lowe (the RAF officer attached to the Research and Experiments Department) the question of low flying attack on factories. Lowe was very worried about the roofs of buildings and agreed that the ideal construction would be to have welded frames with very light cover.

4th November—discussed with Swann (Chief Electrical Inspector of Factories) the protection of electrical undertakings. His view is that far too little is being done for the protection of such very vulnerable gear as transformers and contact breakers. It appears to me that these could easily be protected by welded portal frames with pre-cast block covering if they are to be got at easily.

8th November—saw the officers in charge of ARP Air Ministry, and discussed with them the Air Ministry factories which need strengthening. They appreciate the position and understand what is to be done. It was agreed that I should see three factories for the Air Ministry, examine the drawings and be prepared to give general principles for their protection from collapse. The factories are (1) Vickers, Weybridge (2) Austins Shadow Factory, Birmingham (3) Northern Aluminium Company, Banbury. I stressed the necessity of providing in new construction as much rigidity of the joints as possible, e.g. by welded construction. Also gave as general principles the provision of stanchions under all roof trusses and the introduction of as many extra supports as possible.

9/10th November—visited Bedford, Luton, Northampton and Rugby with Swann.

11th November—letter from the Ministry of Supply, enclosing copies of letters sent to Vauxhall and Thomas Bolton.

13th November—visited Vauxhall Motors, Luton.

15th November—visited Vickers, Weybridge. The most important structure at Vickers is the Flight Shed in which the bombers are assembled. It consists of four deep braced girders approximately 300 feet long, these are carried by transverse girders supported on stanchions at their ends, so that the whole structure depends on four stanchions. If one of these went the roof would collapse. Also if a bomb fell on a girder and demolished a joint or member a large part of the roof would fall. Additional supports are clearly needed. It is, however, essential to keep the floor space clear as once a day planes are moved forward down the shop. Wallis has solved the problem ingeniously by providing under each panel point of the main girders a wooden prop which can in 10 seconds be swung out of the way. This propping system could alone carry the roof with a factor of two. . . . In one shop a gallery supports machines; added resistance to collapse could be obtained if the joists were made continuous over the stanchions by welding.

20/21st November—visited BTH, Rugby, and Northern Aluminium Company, Banbury.

28th November—to Rugby to meet PAD representatives of all the supply Ministries.

Gave them "Notes on the Protection of Vital Factories". They agreed that these should be circulated to designers.

 4th December—attended Co-ordinating Committee, PAD, at Home Office and discussed application of above Notes with representatives again. They agreed that for new factory design designers should be put in touch with me."

Before leaving the extracts from this diary it may be remarked that the swinging props in the Weybridge factory were the only recorded case where a factory manager had taken precautions against collapse. Remembering Barnes Wallis's distinction in many fields of engineering, airship design, the Wellington bomber and the dam-busting bomb, it is hardly surprising that he was the one who had foreseen the danger.

Arising out of the meeting on 4th December a technical sub-committee was formed to the long standing Inter-departmental Committee on ARP in Government Contractors Works. This sub-committee, on which the PAD officers from all the Ministries were represented, met for the first time on 20th December, 1939. The meeting was opened by Dr. Stradling who welcomed, on behalf of the ARP Department of the Ministry of Home Security, the formation of the technical sub-committee which he said would enable the Research and Experiments and Chief Engineers Branches of the ARP Department of the Ministry of Home Security to keep in touch with the PAD Departments of the Services. He promised co-operation in every way possible.

One of the items discussed at this first meeting was the document which had been given to the PAD representatives in Rugby on 28th November and to be published in April 1940 under the title *Strengthening of Structures for Air Attack*, to which reference was made in Chapter 8. It was recorded in Minute No. 13 that:

"Professor Baker replied to certain points raised in connection with his note on the Protection of Vital Factories, and it was agreed that he would amend the note in one or two paragraphs and that revised copies should be supplied as early as possible for issue to designers of vital factories. . . . At the same time it was decided to recommend that in each case the designer of a factory should be asked to get in touch with Professor Baker so that the suggestions indicated in the draft notes could be more adequately explained in view of the fact that the procedure was not at present standard practice among designers of factories and was based on recent research backed by actual work carried out on these lines."

From my point of view the meeting had gone well; after three hectic months all was set fair for advances in protection. I was content. We had revealed a problem of some magnitude and had been able to supply a unique solution; both satisfying steps for an engineer, particularly so in the peculiar twilight condition of those early war months, when many people were merely waiting for the light to dawn or for the lightning to strike. What is more I had made contact with the people who seemed to matter and had secured their ready support for the work. As the representative of the Research and Experiments Branch on the sub-committee I threw myself into its work with enthusiasm.

The technical sub-committee met for the second time on 17th January, 1940. The Minutes compiled by the Secretary, Lt.-Col. F. H. Budden of the Research and Experiments Branch are a salutary reminder that the subject of this book, though perhaps the most important, is only one of the large variety of topics which had to be mastered by the exponents of this emerging branch of engineering, PAD. Twenty-four separate items appear stretching from the standards for cleansing centres (made necessary by the threat of poison gas), through the design of light traps to allow ventiliation in factories working at night, down to an appropriate allowance (agreed at one shilling per cubic foot) for the construction and equipment of first-aid posts. For me, the most important was Item 41 which read:

"The steps that were being taken by the Secretary to publish the notes on the Protection of Vital Factories by Professor Baker and to bring these Notes to the notice of the designers of factories were discussed. It was re-affirmed that everything that could be done to ensure that the steps recommended were adopted wherever possible, should be undertaken."

The sub-committee met at regular monthly intervals until September 1940. At the third and fourth meetings I reported on the results of blast tests carried out at Shoeburyness on windows and offered to fit into the Research and Experiments Department's programme tests at Stewartby on roofing materials and obscuration since the supply Ministries had no funds for tests. At the sixth meeting on 21st May, 1940 the issue of *War-time Building Bulletin No. 1* by the Department of Scientific and Industrial Research was discussed and "the advisability of connecting the PAD branches of the three Services more closely with any future issue was stressed as such publications concerned them more than the departments at present represented on the Building Research Board". At the seventh meeting on 27th June it was reported that I had been appointed an assessor to the Building Research Board so that in all subsequent issues of these important Bulletins the most up-to-date precautions against structural collapse were incorporated. Incidentally, this, the seventh, was the only one of all the thirteen meetings of the sub-committee, that I did not attend; bomb damage in Bristol or elsewhere was probably occupying all my attention.

At the eighth meeting on 23rd July, 1940 when attacks on factories had already become heavy, and production was seriously affected, there was an item of particular interest.

165. The emergency protection of workers in factories

"The chairman had explained the problem which had arisen in connection with the protection of workers in factories as a result of the decision to limit the number of air raid warnings given and referred to the draft memorandum which had been prepared for the Ministry of Labour. Sir Alexander Rouse explained that this memorandum had been drawn up jointly by Mr. B. Barnes, Professor Baker and himself and that it would have to be agreed to with industry before it was finally issued."

Industrial production was being so much reduced by air raids that it had been proposed that workers should not go to the shelters that had been provided for them, usually outside, or on the perimeter of, the factory, when the general air raid alert was sounded but would continue at their benches until their own roof watcher, or "Jim Crow" to use the Prime Minister's term, gave the alarm that the raider was overhead and bombs might be expected immediately. The workers would then take such shelter at, or under, their benches as this Memorandum set out to provide.

This item reminds me of the occasion when, having acted as his technical adviser in this matter, I accompanied the Minister of Labour, Mr. Ernest Bevin, to the meeting of some hundreds of employers and trade union representatives at which that remarkable man persuaded those present to commit their workmen to this highly risky proceeding. Mr. Bevin seemed to know everyone in the room personally and addressed them by their

Christian names. It was a remarkable display of persuasion and diplomacy. One felt that all present trusted this man; that they felt able to commit their employees, or the men they represented, to take the high risks that Bevin demanded is an indication of the remarkable industrial relations that war can bring about.

The ninth meeting was held on 7th August. Emergency protection was again discussed with such mundane information that "there was no possibility of making the cost involved in the provision of emergency protection in factories eligible for any grant". The item with the closest relevance to what was happening up and down the country was the request that copies of any reports of air raid damage to factories should be forwarded to the Research and Experiments Department.

The tenth meeting was originally called for 24th September, 1940. It was postponed to 8th October but in fact did not take place for more than nine months, until 21st May, 1941. When it is remembered that the blitz, which started with the battle of London on 7th September, 1940, became virtually nationwide and continued with ferocity for eight months until early May 1941, one is inclined to applaud a body which decided that this was a time for action and not for sitting around a Committee table. There was action but, unfortunately, it was for the most part ill-advised.

The attempts to provide, by means of the sub-committee, rational direction had virtually come to nothing. Again, but in a much more intense form than with the Ministry of Home Security shelters described in earlier chapters, arose the conflict between harassed ill-informed authority and advisers who, though by no means omniscient, were anxious and able to use scientific methods to solve the many problems facing authority.

Though they were crammed with excitement and made bearable by the work we did in collaboration with Sir Ernest Simon's team, which continued to take us into factories and gave us practical experience, these eight months when formal contact with the PAD sections was interrupted were full of frustration for the Design and Development Section.

I had continued to strive, putting the need for planned protection for industry personally to everyone of influence including Lord Trenchard, Head of the Royal Air Force, Lord Beaverbrook, Minister of Aircraft Production, and through Stradling to the War Cabinet Scientific Advisory Committee at its meeting on 21st October, 1940. I was clearly nearly at the end of my tether by the end of April 1941 when I poured out my troubles in a long Minute to my senior colleague Astbury. This is not surprising when it is remembered that seventeen months had passed since my first meeting with the Heads of the PAD sections, followed by those early enthusiastic sub-committee Minutes, but still no factory structures had been strengthened by them.

My despair was intensified by the failure of our first attempt to produce an all-embracing scheme for the rational direction of factory protection. The document outlining it, dated 31st March, 1941, did not even get out of the Ministry of Home Security.

The minute to Astbury is too long to reproduce in full but extracts will be sufficient to show the state of play and to reflect some of my bitterness. I start by saying that I have not been able to find the real authority for providing protection of plant in factories. It seemed that the heads of the PAD Sections were not only in charge of the inspectors who visited the factories but decided also the policy "In actual fact, of course, there is no policy and none of these gentlemen nor anyone else can make a real decision on policy without the technical assistance of the Research and Experiments Department because we are the only people who can hope to have a sound picture of the effects of bombing. The PAD sections

. . . are staffed by retired army officers most of whom boast that they are not technical men. The rest of the staff is made up mainly of architects and as far as I know only one engineer, he a very young and inexperienced man. I have not met among these quite pleasant people one man of any strong personality and certainly no one of any standing or even reasonable ability in the technical world. . . . There is no doubt that they consider the main part of their job is to see that as little money is spent as possible. . . . They work to what they call a standard. Who set it I cannot imagine. . . . I am perfectly satisfied that they do not understand the problem they are up against even if they know that there is a problem. They are certainly unaware of the grave responsibility which rests on their shoulders." I then remark that the PAD sections are seriously understaffed. ARPAF consisted of 20 inspectors responsible for at least 2000 firms with 4500 separate factories. This meant that no factory could hope to see an inspector for much more than one day every year, which was quite inadequate.

I then deal with shelters. This was a sore subject. I point out that the PAD sections still wish to follow the early Ministry of Home Security shelter standard though I think they should have pushed for better shelter in vital factories. I continue:

"Although we have here a large and competent staff giving for some time undivided attention to the design of improved shelters, these technical men (in the PAD sections) are so small minded that they are incapable in the main of reproducing in their own documents the designs that we have developed after considering all available data from bombing and from actual tests. They always attempt to stamp their personality on their own documents by 'improving' our designs a little", with unfortunate results as I later illustrate.

On protection of structure I say "They have, in fact, completely ignored this work though experience of bombing has shown how right we were. We had warned MAP that such factories as Cunliffe Owen would behave, when it got a bomb in this particular spot, in exactly this way. That advice was given to them at the end of 1939."

On protection of plant I say "The PAD sections do not know what the protection of plant means. They have for some months now been allowing firms to build protective walls but they have made no attempt to study the problem or to plan such protection." I then state what has happened in three individual factories and continue "These cases show that ARPAF, and the same can be said of the Ministry of Supply, have not the first conception of how plant should be protected. Their only solution is to let the firm go to any manufacturer of quack remedies, or even to a local builder and, though perhaps not spending more than the Treasury allows, getting less than no value for that expenditure.

"The Research and Experiments Department had, by dint of its own exertions established close collaboration with the MAP Emergency Services Organisation and in particular have helped the North Western Area MAP (Sir Ernest Simon's team). We have thus been able to give our latest ideas on protection of plant to that area. ARPAF far from welcoming this opportunity of greater efficiency, resent this direct contact."

Then I end with a heartfelt peroration which shows how seriously I was taking myself and RE4's work, saying "As today the war cannot be won on the battlefield until it is won first in the workshops, if more active steps are not taken to reduce the effect of enemy action, we will soon be brought to our knees".

In the calm engendered by the passage of 37 years, one cannot help sympathising with ARPAF at their resentment of our activities in their North Western region. However, changes were about to be made there. In May 1941 Sir Peter Bennett, Director General of Emergency Services Organisation (MAP), carried out some reorganisation. It was rumoured that Mr. Brian Colquhoun, at that time Director-General of Aircraft Production Factories, would be put in charge of ARPAF but eventually that responsibility was given to Mr. Francis Smith, an architect member of the ESO who was already running the recently formed Fire Protection Section of MAP.

CHAPTER 10

Blast Walls

The technical sub-committee of the Inter-Departmental Committee on ARP in Government Contractors Works met again at 4.30 p.m. on 21st May, 1941. Nothing was recorded in the Minutes of this tenth meeting to explain the nine months gap or to suggest why the sub-committee had troubled to come together again. There was, of course, no hint of Sir Peter Bennett's concern about the organisation of ARPAF, though I had had my second meeting with him that day, but it was clear that much had been happening behind the scenes and some of the most worrying aspects of the defence of factories, poured out to Astbury in April, were being resolved. This is shown by the first Minute of the meeting which read:

"191. *Shelters*

The question of what general recommendations should be made to factories concerning the provision of shelters was discussed and it was agreed to recommend that (a) All shelters should be constructed of reinforced concrete or reinforced brickwork."

The next two Minutes were also important.

"192. The Chairman explained that he had been in touch with Princes Risborough concerning the most suitable form of blast walls and wished to ensure that similar standards were adopted for the PAD departments of the three Services. After a discussion of the difficulties that were encountered in factories in connection with the provision of blast walls it was agreed that:

(a) The old standard of protection required against a 500 lb bomb at 50 feet should be dropped and that it should be noted that a higher standard was required.

(b) All blast walls should be constructed of reinforced brick or reinforced concrete or their equivalent. These and all other walls should be adequately buttressed or otherwise supported laterally.

In this connection Professor Baker promised to supply type designs.

193. *Existing brick shelters*

Professor Baker promised to issue as early as possible advice concerning the strengthening of existing brick shelters."

The principal item at the eleventh meeting held on 19th June was a discussion of "blast" walls for which advance copies of a note on recent development in protective wall design for factories had been circulated. Much effort was to be devoted in the next three months to this subject so it will be well to examine it in some detail.

It was recorded in Chapter 9 that during the first three months of 1941 the supply Ministries encouraged the building of blast walls in factories. It may be said bluntly that the same mistake was made in this first generation of walls as in the first generation of surface shelters, but with less excuse. They were almost without exception built of brittle material, either brickwork or hollow blocks, and usually with no more buttress than was common in a garden wall. It is unkind to suggest that they must have been popularly called "blast" walls because they were so easily knocked down by the blast from a distant bomb and became added missiles when the bomb was close. A wall subjected to a near bomb explosion might fail by being shattered into fragments forming destructive missiles, by overturning, causing serious casualties to workers taking emergency shelter and in damage to plant, or by being blown bodily across the shop sweeping all before it.

The Design and Development Section set out to lessen the possibility of these sources of failure, to produce improved, efficient protective walls of various kinds which could be relied upon to protect vital plant from bomb fragments and other missiles caused by a 250 kg bomb exploding 20 feet away. The work need not be described in great detail because it followed very closely the steps taken, rather less than a year before, in producing the improved designs of surface shelters. The principles governing the work were the same—continuity and ductility to absorb the energy—with an additional safeguard that the resistance of the component parts of the wall were graded so that under excessive blast the wall would bend over, or for a buttressed wall tip up, without disintegrating and becoming dangerous missiles. The designs were all proved by careful full-scale tests carried out at Stewartby. A Bulletin B10 "Protective walls in single-storey factories" was ready by early September 1941 and contained details and working drawings for any height and span of four essentially different types of fixed protective walls and for a movable wall.

The fixed types comprised:

(a) A buttress wall of reinforced brick or concrete built on the floor surface—suitable for construction in existing factories where space permitted and there were objections to opening up the ground—illustrated in Fig. 10.1.

(b) A vertical reinforced concrete slab partly embedded in the ground—particularly suitable for projected factories and where extra high walls were required.

(c) A wall comprising reinforced brick or concrete panels held at intervals by vertical steel supports partly embedded in the ground—suitable for construction in existing factories where space was restricted but conditions permitted post supports being driven or sunk, Fig. 10.2.

(d) A similar wall except that the steel supports took the form of inverted T's standing in or on the floor instead of being cantilevers as in Fig. 10.2—suitable for construction in existing factories where space was restricted.

The movable wall, intended to permit the passage of large products such as aircraft down the line of production, consisted of a series of inverted V shaped steel frames on wheels, covered with reinforced concrete panels, designed to nest, illustrated in Fig. 10.3.

Fig. 10.4 shows a buttressed wall in a Leamington factory which had behaved perfectly and right up to the limit of its capacity, thereby saving a store of valuable components which were stacked on the side of the wall away from the explosion.

The last part of the design and testing programme was the development of reliable methods of strengthening sub-standard walls. They were sub-standard because they were unreinforced, without buttresses or too low. As with the strengthening of unreinforced surface shelters the most effective method consisted in adding to each face of the wall a 3 inch thickness of reinforced concrete bonded to the existing brickwork. Where necessary the wall was raised by carrying up the vertical reinforcement of the skins and casting concrete to form the additional height and additional buttresses.

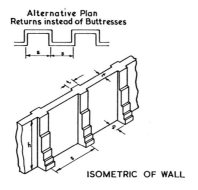

Alternative Plan
Returns instead of Buttresses

ISOMETRIC OF WALL

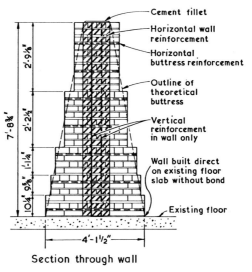

Cement fillet

Horizontal wall
reinforcement

Horizontal
buttress reinforcement

Outline of
theoretical
buttress

Vertical
reinforcement
in wall only

Wall built direct
on existing floor
slab without bond

Existing floor

Section through wall

Fig. 10.1

Heated arguments took place in committee on the height of walls required. The PAD inspectors thought they need only be the same height as the plant they were to protect but RE4 knew, from studying the reports of raid damage, that about half the enemy bombs were fused to explode on contact with the factory roof. This demanded higher walls and Bulletin B10 contained a formula for the best height, a function of the height of the plant and of the factory roof. It was demonstrated that for the same cost a few high walls were more efficient than several low ones.

We in the Design and Development Section were not at this time convinced that the provision of walls was the best way of protecting production, though we had ensured, by introducing efficient designs, that if they were used they did not become additional missiles. Walls had come into existence as an instinctive move to provide cover, to reduce that unpleasant feeling that came, particularly at night, in a large single-storey factory of being caught defenceless in a wide open space. With the new policy of working after the air-raid alert, mentioned in Minute 165 (Chapter 9), there was obviously much to be said for them as protection, or at least comfort, for the workers; for the plant we were not so certain.

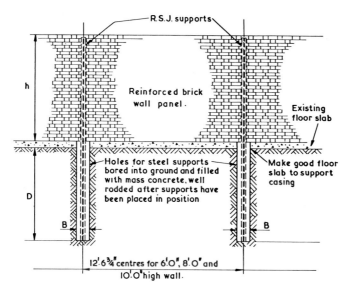

Fig. 10.2

To mark this the Bulletin contained a section on planning considerations; we were obviously beginning to develop a rational approach to the problem. The section will be quoted briefly to show how far our limited experience allowed us to go.

"If a particular sum of money has been allocated for a protective scheme the problem will be to provide the highest possible standard of protection within the limits fixed.

The design of a protective scheme for a factory or industrial process should follow a rational sequence.

(1) There are key points on which the production process depends, e.g. jig borers, machine cutters, tool and instrument stores. Vital machines and tools of this type must

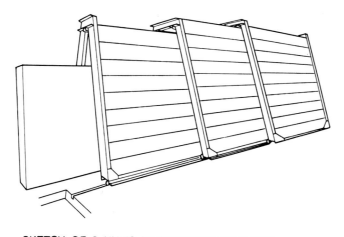

SKETCH OF 3 UNITS IN EXTENDED POSITION

Fig. 10.3

Fig. 10.4

be given a higher standard of protection than the rest of the plant. This protection should incorporate overhead cover. This is best provided by a framed portal structure fixed to the floor, an example is shown (this was my original steel portal surface shelter, shown in Fig. 5.1, but, of course, without the unreinforced ends which fell off under test).

(2) The lay-out of most factories can be divided into zones, such as raw material stores, tool maintenance and storage, machine tool shops, assembly processes, component and finished products stores.

Since each zone forms a link in the chain of production it is clearly desirable that the chain should be duplicated lest production be stopped by the destruction of a vital link. Hence before planning a system of protective walls the possibilities of dispersion within the factory should be thoroughly examined.

Where dispersion cannot be carried out effectively the risk of production stoppage can be reduced by providing protective walls *through* the zone so as to divide the zone into separate units. Each unit should contain a representative selection of the contents of the zone. For example in machine tool shops instead of concentrating all machine tools of a particular type into one unit each unit should contain a proportion of the various types of machine tools so that production could be continued through a single unit. The same principle should be applied to stores and so forth. In general, therefore, it will be found preferable to provide protective walls *through* zones rather than at *boundaries* of zones.

If a zone contains three or four similar production lines and if cost will allow only one wall per zone the wall should be placed down the centre of the zone, i.e. parallel to the production lines."

The real difficulty in carrying our rational approach further was to know what was the appropriate "sum of money" referred to in the first line of the above extract. Neither RE4 nor anyone else knew what this was though there were some influential people, notably Mr. Brian Colquhoun, the Director-General of Aircraft Production Factories, who held the strong view that it was nothing.

To show how Mr. Colquhoun was reached, the story of my campaign for the strengthening of factory structures must be taken up again briefly. It is pleasant to do so because after the somewhat querulous account already given, it is possible to record some slight success. This was mainly due to Ramsay Moon, the Secretary of the Welding Institute who, as mentioned in Chapter 4, had provided Roderick's salary for our pre-war research. Moon had succeeded in setting up in the Ministry of Supply a welding advisory service to further the use of this relatively new method of joining steel members. He had recruited a structural engineer, Helsby, who interested the Ministry of Works and Buildings in the possibility of using welding to strengthen factory buildings. This came to the notice of Hugh Beaver, Director-General and Controller-General of that Ministry. He thought highly of the proposal and in August 1941 invited me to serve on yet another committee to consider the possibilities of widespread strengthening. This was under the Chairmanship of Guthlac Wilson, the Director of Constructional Design in the Ministry, a young man who, after the war, was to join my friend W. L. Scott, mentioned in Chapter 8, as a partner in his consulting firm. This Committee had grandiose ideas about engaging 200 welders and strengthening $3\frac{1}{2}$ million square yards of factory per month at an average cost of £75 per thousand square yards. In its turn this effort probably got bogged down in the Civil Service morass because there is a memorandum of a visit I paid to London on 1st December, 1941; it reads "Called to see Ramsay Moon and learned that . . . a great drive was being made for strengthening steelwork".

The important by-product of the effort, however, was that through Guthlac Wilson I came into contact with Colquhoun whose reactions are revealed in a letter I wrote to Guthlac Wilson on 27th October, 1941 as follows:

"I am surprised that no one at MAP has told Mr. Colquhoun of their Southampton factory Cunliffe Owen, which is the classic case of spreading collapse. This is shown in example 1 attached and needs little explanation. One hundred and five thousand square feet of the building collapsed. Our opinion is that this was caused by the one bomb marked "A" although the others may have been slightly contributory in stripping the sheeting. The cost of bracing to prevent this collapse which MAP inserted when the factory was rebuilt was a very small fraction of the total cost.

Another MAP factory which has suffered serious spreading collapse of about 50 000 square feet is Vickers, Blackpool. This is shown in example 2. This resulted in my opinion, from the failure of a stanchion and although it was not due to enemy action it is exactly what would have happened had a 250 kg or larger bomb exploded within a radius of 15 feet of any stanchion.

Two other cases of considerable, but preventable, collapse are shown in examples 3 and 4. Strangely enough, as far as I know, no hit has been recorded on the type of building vertically glazed with north light trusses carried on apex lattice girders which first brought the danger of spreading collapse to our notice, and which should provide the most spectacular examples. This immunity I think you will agree is not due to this particular form of construction and is not a sound reason for failing to guard against the danger! I hope these examples will serve Mr. Beaver's purpose, at least they show that the hypothetical interference with existing production is not an entirely groundless assumption.

We have records of many cases of bad damage to steelwork involving as much as 8000 square feet, not strictly of the "spreading" variety which the precautions we recommend would have prevented. If you are interested you should come out here and inspect the reports. I am not aware of any case of damage where our estimates of the danger of spreading collapse have been proved alarmist. . . . As you say Mr. Colquhoun has pretty wide opportunities to see the effects of bomb damage but may I remind you that we are saddled with the duty of investigating all cases of damage and that is a job which needs very great care if misleading conclusions are to be avoided.

As I have told you, my opinion is that this strengthening of structure should only be carried out in conjunction with the protection of plant and products by means of walls and other devices, the design and planning of which has now a rational basis. Both these precautions need labour and materials which could be used for new buildings. The percentage of the available labour and material to be expended on structural precautions to give optimum production at any time, taking into account the interference due to enemy air attack, has little, if anything, to do with the total labour and material available, as Mr. Colquhoun suggests. It depends on the weight of the enemy attack to be expected and on the efficiency of the protection. If no attack is to be expected no protection should be provided. If the attack is to be very heavy all labour and material should be used to provide protection.

A study to determine the correct expenditure within the above limits is urgently needed. It must be based on the facts and on the estimate of future attacks, not on personal opinions. As the Ministry of Works and Buildings controls building you must be vitally concerned with such a study."

I met Colquhoun as the following memorandum records:

Professor Baker's visit to London 4th November, 1941

"I saw Mr. McClaren, Ministry of Aircraft Production, and met Mr. Colquhoun, Director-General of Aircraft Factories, and Mr. W. R. Watson, Deputy-Director.

We had a frank discussion of the position of protection in aircraft factories. Mr.

Colquhoun stated that the Prime Minister had demanded a certain bomber production and that the building labour and material was scarcely sufficient for the building of new factories to give this production. He was, therefore, loath to expend any labour on protection. He would prefer to build a factory without protection and have it in production by June next year and then, if the labour were available, to add the protection. I pointed out that this was a possible method but that it would be essential to plan the protection in the first place, otherwise an attempt to provide additional protection in June would very probably interfere with production. I drew Mr. Colquhoun's attention to the fact that a certain production had been demanded and that if enemy air attack were appreciable this production could be more certainly obtained by giving protection in certain factories rather than by concentrating all the building material on new and unprotected factories. Mr. Colquhoun was sympathetic to this view and is, I think, prepared now to consider the possibility of giving additional protection in aircraft factories. I assured him that our work now had a rational basis and that we could give advice on any subject of defence. In my opinion the best thing was for some of his men to come down here and be instructed and he agreed that his deputy, Mr. Watson, and at least one other member of his staff would come down in the week beginning 10th November.

Mr. Colquhoun was also anxious that a meeting should take place between himself and Mr. Francis Smith and myself. I think this meeting might be left until Mr. Watson has visited Princes Risborough."

It is clear that at last some headway was being made and that those in authority were beginning to realise that under active war conditions their thinking and actions had been somewhat muddled.

The best way I could think of resolving the muddle was, of course, for RE4 to take charge of the whole operation. I engaged with Stradling in a mild struggle for greater recognition. Whether I realised it at the time or not, what I hankered after was some executive power. RE4 had the knowledge, what I wanted was to be able to go out and see that it was applied. I was tired of struggling from one interview with a Director of This to a Director of That and occasionally seeing a Director-General or Controller-General of something else, usually without much effect. I sank so low as to believe that the work of the Section would be more effective if I joined this throng, as a Minute to Stradling, undated, but probably of June 1941, shows. Its chief interest lies in a list attached of the members of RE4. This is reproduced as an Appendix at the end of this Chapter so that it will be clear who had been carrying out the great mass of work in these first two years of the war. The Minute began:

"Referring to our conversation of a few days ago and the difficulty you found in setting out the case to go to the Treasury, might I suggest this as a possible way." Then follows a fairly detailed account of all that the Section had done, not only on shelter design for Home Security, but on pioneering work for the protection of production for all the other Ministries and for a large number of individual firms and consulting engineers "running into millions of pounds", the Minute ending:

"In view of the nature and responsibility of the work and its rapidly increasing volume, I recommend that a new post, that of Director of Design and Development should be established at a salary of . . ." There is no record of any reply from Stradling.

My next move was a document dated 8th August, 1941 marked "Secret—Defence of

Industry, Suggested Organisation". After two short paragraphs outlining the existing organisation of the independent PAD sections the document continues:

"There have been rapid developments in methods of defence arising out of the experience of the 'blitzes' and of research and investigation. These developments are continually under review at the Research and Experiments Department and to ensure that they are properly co-ordinated and passed out with the greatest speed and efficiency it is proposed that a Committee consisting of one member from each of the three Ministries mentioned and one from Research and Experiments Department, Ministry of Home Security should be formed with a technical secretary from Research and Experiments Department. It will be the duty of this Committee to set out the general principles with such detail as it may feel is necessary for the defence of industry against air attack, issuing recommendations which will be used by all three Ministries when the subject makes it possible. It is important that the Committee should be so constituted that it can advise Treasury on technical matters bearing on the expenditure to be incurred in the defence of industry and it should, of course, be the body to which Treasury send PAD schemes for approval. It will be a great advantage if Treasury can send a member to the Committee. Developments in this field since the publication of the pamphlet *ARP for Government Contractors* have been so far reaching and must be so elastic as to accommodate changes in enemy tactics that it is impossible to instruct the inspectors who guide firms adequately by written recommendation and bulletins. It is proposed, therefore, that groups of inspectors should be sent to Research and Experiments Department for refresher courses. While there, in addition to being instructed in the latest principles, they can be employed in the preparation of one of the complete schemes of protection which the Research and Experiments Department undertakes for particular firms. Once the scheme outlined above is working satisfactorily the corresponding problem of the defence of those firms which are not Government contractors must be considered."

Though this may not have been as sweeping a reorganisation as I desired it appealed to my seniors. It led to a letter, dated 26th August, 1941, from Sir George Gater, Secretary of the Ministry of Home Security, to the Secretaries of all the other Ministries. It read:

"Sir, I am directed by the Minister of Home Security to say that on the suggestion of the Passive Air Defence officers of the supply Ministries he has had under consideration the question how the knowledge of the effects of German bombing which has been acquired by the Research and Experiments Department of this Ministry can best be made available to the departments responsible for the control and erection of factories engaged on important Government work. As a result of informal discussions between representatives of this Ministry, the supply departments and the Treasury, the Minister is of opinion that it would be useful to set up a small committee under the Chairmanship of the deputy secretary of the Ministry of Home Security on which the Treasury, Admiralty, Ministry of Supply, Ministry of Aircraft Production, Ministry of Works and Buildings and the Chief Engineer and the Research and Experiments Department of this Ministry would be represented by senior technical officers and I am to invite the Minister of . . . if he agrees, to be good enough to nominate a representative to such a Committee.

The Committee would consider from time to time the results of the observations and experiments of the Research and Experiments Department and discuss the nature of the instructions to be issued to factories and inspectorates having regard to the cost of the measures recommended and the degree of insurance against damage and interference with production which such measures might be expected to secure.

In addition the Minister suggests that in order that the Inspectors of the various supply departments may be kept in close touch with current knowledge and development, it would be useful to establish a refresher course in connection with Professor Baker's section of the Research and Experiments Department at Princes Risborough to which inspectors could be sent for instruction and practical training. It is thought that a period of at least one month would be necessary in each case so that each inspector could, as part of the course, work out in collaboration with Professor Baker's section a scheme for some installation for which he was responsible. By this means really effective training would be secured. The Minister will be glad to learn as soon as possible whether this proposal is acceptable to you. Details can then be arranged departmentally.

I am, Sir,

Your obedient Servant,

G. H. Gater."

The proposal was acceptable to the other Ministers with the result that the Factory (PAD) Committee came into being on 18th November, 1941. Its story will be told in Chapter 11.

I made one last attack on Stradling, writing to him on 17th October, 1941. "When last we discussed the responsibility in the Ministry of Home Security for questions concerning the defence of industry, you told me that you had been waiting for Treasury sanction before defining my position as Chief Design and Development Engineer. You agreed, however, that in view of the regrettable delay by the Treasury, the matter should not be put off any longer.

I understand from Mr. Astbury that the new Committee (i.e. the Factory (PAD) Committee) may meet soon. In view of this and of the increased part we are playing in the affairs of ARPAF and PAD, Ministry of Supply, I feel it imperative that my position and responsibilities should be defined without loss of time."

Nothing happened so I continued to the end unsupported by anything more than my courtesy title of "Professor", of which I have always been proud even if to this day, it is a slight handicap when dealing with most people in British industry.

APPENDIX

Members of RE4, the Design and Development Section,
Research and Experiments Department, Ministry of Home Security, June 1941

Name	Grade	Salary	Name	Grade	Salary
Prof. J. F. Baker	Scientific Adviser	£1000	Mr. G. S. M. Grimmer	Engineer	£600
			Mr. A. Beedle	,,	£600
Mr. A. R. Astbury	Technical Adviser	£850	Mr. D. C. Burn	,,	£750
			Mr. F. H. Pavry	,,	£500
Mr. Basil Ward	Architect	£700	Miss E. C. J. Mather	Temporary Assistant	£170
Mr. C. A. Lucas	,,	£550			
Miss A. Dicker	,,	£400	Mr. Cullingford	Production Officer	£500
Mr. H. C. Hughes	,,	£600			
Mr. R. L. Townsend	,,	£450	Mrs. G. Adams	Draughtsman	£3 p.w.

Mr. L. M. Desyllas	Junior Architect	£350	Mr. S. M. Sternfeldt	,,	£7 p.w.
Mr. J. H. Madge	,,	£350	Mr. H. Simpson	TMC	To scale
Mr. Leader-Williams	Senior Engineer	£700	Miss K. Coatsworth	Mapping Assistant	£166
Mr. N. J. Durant	,,	£650	Miss B. E. M. C. Stillwell	TWC II	To scale
Mr. P. A. Badland	Engineer	£500	Mr. E. M. Granger	TMC	,, ,,
Mr. D. Lax	,,	£600	Mrs. L. D. Farmer	S/Typist	,, ,,
			Miss D. G. Barratt	,,	,, ,,

CHAPTER 11

The Factory (PAD) Committee

The technical sub-commitee was to have held its fourteenth meeting on 18th September, 1941 but on 11th September a note was circulated to members saying "The meeting for Thursday 18th September is postponed in view of the Chairman's resignation. A decision on the future of the technical sub-committee is awaited."

Sir Peter Bennett's reorganisation of ARPAF and Sir George Gater's letter of 26th August had had their effect with the result that the sub-committee was replaced by the Factory (PAD) Committee under the Chairmanship of Harold Scott, now Deputy-Secretary of the Ministry of Home Security. It had a standing sub-committee of which I was Chairman. As envisaged by Gater the Committee consisted of representatives from the Ministries of Supply, Aircraft Production, Works and Buildings, Home Security, the Admiralty and Treasury.

The Committee met for the first time on 18th November, 1941. The first paper presented to it by RE4 was entitled "A Note on the Standard of Protection for Buildings and Plant". Compared with the practical design Bulletins which had come from my Section in the past this read more like an academic exercise. It was an attempt to get down to the fundamentals of a problem, the detailed parameters of which were unknown, at least to the Research and Experiments Department. Looked at from this distance in time it has some of the marks of a coat-trailing exercise.

The Paper began:

"(1) The purpose of this Note is to show how a rational method can be applied to the determination of the economic standard of protection which should be given to a factory to make it less vulnerable to air attack.

It is self-evident that the economic standard depends on the scale of air attack to be expected. If there is to be no bombing, maximum production in the shops will be obtained by allotting all available building labour and material to the construction of new factories, and none to protective devices. What is not so obvious is that the proportion of the available material and labour, which should be expended on protection if there is to be bombing, is independent of the total amount of labour and material available.

(2) Consider first the case where all available labour and material are used to build and equip new factories. If Z is the number of existing factories, and m is the number of new factories finished in a given period, then if a raid of intensity $p\%$ (i.e. one which knocks out $p\%$ of factories) is experienced at the end of this period, the number of factories available for production is

$$(Z + m)(1 - p') \tag{1}$$
where $p' = p/100$

(3) Suppose now that all the labour and material had been used in providing protective devices in the existing factories. If protection costs $1/n$ of new work (i.e. n factories could be protected for every new one built) and this standard of protection cuts the risk of damage to $1/q$ that in an unprotected factory (i.e. the plant in only one protected factory would be knocked out in a raid which puts q unprotected factories out of production) then, under the same conditions assumed in § (2) above, the number of factories available for production will be

$$(Z - mn)(1 - p') + mn - mnp'/q \qquad (2)$$

(4) Comparing expressions (1) and (2), it will be seen that using all labour and material on protection makes more factories available after the raid if

$$(p' - p'/q) n > 1 - p' \qquad (3)$$

$$\text{or if } p' > \frac{1}{(1 + n - n/q)}$$

That is to say, it will pay to put everything into protection if the intensity of raid is greater than

$$\frac{100}{(1 + n - n/q)} \%$$

This, it is interesting to note, is independent of m the number of new factories which could be built, and therefore of the labour and material available.

(5) The simple case dealt with in §§ 2–4 above may appear artificial, but it is roughly the condition which might arise if the enemy chose to attack at the same time all factories of one type, e.g. bomber assembly works. The critical percentage attack can only be evaluated when n and q are known. They cannot be estimated accurately here since present-day values of plant, etc., are not available, but upper and lower limit values will be suggested. The cost of protective measures varies from shop to shop, but a possible figure for the standard of protection which would make q equal to 5 is about £500 per 1000 square yard of shop. The cost of this area of new building might be as high today as £5000 so that considering the value of factory building alone, n would be 10, so that the critical weight of attack would be

$$\frac{100}{(1 + 10 - 2)} \% \text{ or } 11\tfrac{1}{9}\%$$

This is, however, probably a gross underestimate of the value of n, since plant must be considered as well as buildings. The value of plant of certain kinds might be so high as to make 100 a fairer value for n. The critical value of p would then be 1.23%.

It should be noted that the percentage p is not particularly sensitive to variations in q. In this last case, if the protective measures only reduced the damage in protected factories by one-half that in unprotected, p would still be less than 2%."

The rest of the paper was devoted to the more complicated and possibly more practical assumption that raids occurred at successive intervals while factories continued to be built and protection to be provided. The expressions were correspondingly more complicated and will not be reproduced here but a general condition could again be written down showing under what intensity of raiding greater production could be obtained, over a given time, by concentrating on protection. The condition was again independent of m and therefore of the amount of labour and material available. This, of course, was the most important conclusion in the paper. We were too ignorant at this time to put accurate values on the factors n and q but whatever they might be, we had demonstrated that when the raiding intensity p rose above a certain value then, however small building resources might be, greater production would result from using them on protection.

We did not allow our ignorance to prevent us drawing some colourful conclusions, for instance that in the central three square miles of Birmingham, where for a period of eight months from 15th October, 1940 to 15th June, 1941, the intensity of bombing was 3% per month (one bomb in every area 180 feet square constituting 100%), it would have paid to enclose a piece of vital plant in a protective structure, which would have cost £150 to build, if the cost of the plant and its production had exceeded £726. Likewise a shed building in the same area liable to spreading collapse should have been strengthened at a cost of £10 000 if the building and its contents had been worth more than £62 500, when in fact they would have been worth several millions of pounds.

At the second meeting of the Committee held on 23rd December, 1941, Francis Smith, the representative of the Ministry of Aircraft Production, said he had passed the Paper to his Statistical and Production Departments for their comments. In the meantime he had collected certain statistical data which showed that over a period of 12 months the loss in productive capacity of machine tools due to air attack had been about 1.3%. Naturally there were wide variations from this figure when particular factories were considered. After discussion it was decided that the Research and Experiments Department would investigate with the Production and Finance Departments the practicability of evaluating particular degrees of protection.

However, before this could bear fruit, John Madge discovered that one of his teachers at Cambridge, E. A. G. Robinson,[1] was a member of the War Cabinet Office (Economics Section). He took our Paper to show him.

Robinson produced a note, dated 2nd December, in which he said: "Professor Baker's Note carried the discussion of the principles which should govern the use of building labour for protection of buildings and plant an important stage further. But he has necessarily and inevitably done so by a process of simplification and generalisation. To go forward again, it is necessary to consider in what respects he has over-simplified the problem.

"There are, I think, two main respects in which he has done this:

"(a) He has assumed that the alternatives are, on the one hand, an increase in the number of unspecialised factories to produce the same things as are already produced, and on the other hand the protection of the existing number of factories;

"(b) he has assumed a uniform standard of protection related (in his initial calculations) to the cost of the building alone, and has assumed that this uniform expenditure reduces all risks to a uniform proportion $1/q$."

[1] Now Professor Sir Austin Robinson, CMG., FBA., Emeritus Professor of Economics, Cambridge University.

Robinson then examines in more detail some of these over-simplifications without substituting any more complex or exact criteria and ends his note:

"These criticisms should, however, not be permitted to obscure the main results of Professor Baker's Paper. He has shown that, in a simplified case, even if attention is confined to the value of the building itself, a cost of protection equal to 10% of the initial cost is justified within 12 months of raiding of the intensity which Birmingham suffered last year, and that even with an intensity one third of that it would be justified in little more than two years. If value of machinery and work in progress were together equal to twice that of the building (probably a conservative estimate) 1% raiding would justify protection in about a year. Even if full allowance is made for the further considerations that have been discussed in this paper, there is little doubt that the conclusion is justified that protection has not hitherto been carried as far as it should."

This was followed next day by a further communication:

"Since I wrote my note on this Paper yesterday, I have attended a meeting at the Ministry of Aircraft Production at which there were present various officials of that Ministry concerned with factory building and protection as well as Mr. Cairncross[2] and Mr. Champernowne[3] from the Directorate of Statistics.

We discussed rather briefly Professor Baker's Paper and there was, I think, general agreement that while it was of great theoretical interest it considerably over-simplified the real problems and that his theoretical criteria could not be applied in practice.

We then proceeded to discuss the practical possibilities and I record these while they are fresh in my mind.

It was the impression of those present that a considerable amount of protection had already been done, but done rather unsystematically and not to as high a standard as was now being proposed. It would, however, probably not pay to improve the protection where this was already complete. In new factories again a certain amount of protection was being put in, but this also was not up to the standard now being proposed. It was also agreed that there were considerably differing priorities for the protection of different factories. Some bottleneck processes in bottleneck factories had clearly a very high priority indeed; in others the priority must be regarded as rather low.

We attempted to work out by rather rough and ready methods the amount of manpower which might properly be devoted to this task. We made, on the spur of the moment, and with very inadequate statistics, two rough calculations, both of which led to broadly the same order of magnitude of conclusion. First we may assume that protection is necessary roughly for a million engineering workers. These will each be using about 150 square feet of space constructed newly at a cost of about £150. It was agreed that the required standard of protection would cost about one tenth of new construction thus a total expenditure of about £15 000 000 might be justified.

Secondly, we calculated that the total value of existing factories at their original cost of production was probably between £750 000 000 and £1 000 000 000. If about 20% of these required protection the cost would be some £15–20 000 000.

£15 000 000 can be converted into about 300 000 man-months. That is to say, altogether the full measure of protection would require some 25 000 workers for a

[2] Now Sir Alec Cairncross, KCMG, FBA., Master of St. Peter's College, Oxford, formerly Head of the Government Economic Service.

[3] Now Professor D. G. Champernowne, FBA., Professor of Economics and Statistics, Cambridge University.

period of twelve months. This is, in fact, little more than one third of the numbers that have hitherto been employed on shelters and static water.

In the case of factory protection, on the other hand, there is a quite substantial quid pro quo to set on the other side. The value of machine tools completely destroyed or repaired (at the cost of repair) during the last year is about £4 000 000. The standard of protection suggested should have saved £3 000 000 of this damage. In doing so, it would have saved the work for the year of somewhere about 3000 to 4000 of the most highly skilled engineering workers. It would have saved also a great deal of work in progress and would have greatly reduced the loss of output due to actual damage of tools. This we hope it may be possible to measure, though there are statistical difficulties. The Ministry of Aircraft Production officials are also convinced that it will have important repercussions on the loss of time due to alerts and due to absenteeism following raids. One must also bring in on the credit side the reduced damage to the building itself if the explosion is localised.

It is clearly not possible to set out the full balance sheet, but it is evident that a capital expenditure of some £15 000 000 of building labour might very easily be covered over a period of two years by an equal saving in money spent on much more scarce types of skilled and semiskilled engineering labour, including that of the particularly scarce tool makers and tool repairers.

I think we were all persuaded that there was a strong *prima facie* case for increased expenditure on factory protection. The source from which this building labour should be drawn is less clear and the others present did not feel competent to discuss it in detail."

These notes from Robinson endorsing the views of other distinguished economists were immensely helpful. For the first time an independent expert had reported on the proposals put forward so vigorously for so long by the members of the Design and Development Section. Our standing was immediately enhanced, not only in the eyes of the supply Ministries but of our senior Home Security colleagues whose support in forming the Factory (PAD) Committee had, it must be admitted, been more loyal than enthusiastic. Now the prospect of obtaining sound values for the constants in the formulae of our Paper were greatly improved.

At the third meeting of the Committee held on 24th February, 1942 it was reported that the investigation of the practicability of evaluating particular degrees of protection was in hand. The Ministry of Aircraft Production had been consulted and one vital branch of the aircraft industry comprising four factories had been selected. Some unexplained snag arose so attention was transferred to the carburettor industry and satisfactory arrangements were made with three firms for surveys of their works.

In the end two factories, SU Carburettors and Hobson's Carburettors were surveyed in detail. The first was fully reported in a document, FC 23, dated 19th May, 1942. The report on the Hobson survey was not published but its results were incorporated in a document (FC 23A) "Summary and Recommendations based on surveys of two factories manufacturing aircraft carburettors" dated 27th May, 1942.

The report on the SU Carburettors survey is too long to reproduce here. This is unfortunate because it describes such original and imaginative work that it should be available in full to take its proper place in the history of production engineering.

In describing work of this kind, carried out by such a closely knit war-time team as the Design and Development Section, it is invidious to single out names, particularly after a lapse of more than thirty years. An early typed draft of the Hobson report which has survived carries the initials of G. S. C. Grimmer and is marked for circulation to Madge, Beedle, Leader-Williams and Baker, while attached sheets carry information or comments from Desyllas, Lax and Pavry. However, there is no doubt that John Madge and E. Leader-Williams played the most prominent parts.

Madge, at that time a young architect but later to become a distinguished sociologist, had come down from Cambridge, where he had read economics as well as architecture, just before the war started. He was a tall, slim, long-haired elegant young man; not the type one would have instinctively chosen to interview tough works managers. However, it was a great experience to survey a works with him; in no time at all he gained the confidence of even the most harassed works manager, who not only told him all about the production flow but was quick to take his advice. It was no uncommon experience for the Research and Experiments team to see machine tools being regrouped even before we left the works to write our report.

Leader-Williams, owing to his disability, was bound to the office but he acted as a ready foil to Madge. He revealed a most useful mastery of the theory of probabilities, unusual in a structural engineer. If I had not known him intimately from his undergraduate days I would have suspected that he had mis-spent his youth on the race-course.

The first step in a survey was an estimate of the output of the factory which would be lost if any one machine tool was damaged, loss of output depending on the importance of the machine tool and the time taken to replace it. The importance of the machine tool was bound up with the production method and about this the management was consulted before any figures were estimated. It is difficult to remember what, in 1939, was the state of the art of management consultancy but these preliminary discussions must have been close to those which a peace-time consultant would have developed. Whatever may have been the final success in protecting production from bombs, there is no doubt that the penetrating questions asked during a survey sometimes revealed shortcomings in lay-out or production flow which the management was quick to correct to the great benefit of production efficiency.

In the SU Carburettor survey, the effect of a bomb exploding at floor level or in the roof anywhere on the unprotected factory was determined by dividing the factory into 36 feet by 36 feet squares, the grid being applied to the factory plan at a random angle. It was assumed that each floor bomb damaged all tools within a square of side 36 feet and similarly each roof bomb damaged all tools within a square of side 72 feet. A table was drawn up showing the effect on the unprotected factory of a bomb hit at each of the grid intersections. The summation of the table gave a figure for the total loss if one bomb fell at each point on the bomb grid. This total is, of course, imaginary since if the factory were hit by more than one bomb the damage might overlap and reduce the total. The sum can, however, be used to determine the average effect of a hit anywhere on the factory. Thus a bomb at each of the 114 grid points caused a loss of (say) 154 458 units of production and therefore the average direct hit on the factory would cause a loss of 154 458/114 = 1350 units.

Similarly this result could be used to determine the probable loss due to raiding of any given intensity. The area covered by the factory was 148 000 square feet and therefore if it were subjected to a raiding intensity of one bomb in 100 000 square feet it would probably be hit by 1.48 bombs and the loss of output would be 1.48 by 1350 or 2000 units.

The exercise was repeated after various protective measures had been introduced. These consisted of straight runs of different lengths and arrangements of the highly efficient protective walls described in Chapter 10 and three-, or even on occasion four-sided pens formed from walls round individual machines. The structure of the factory could also be strengthened to minimise collapse. The cost of these measures and the saving in production resulting from each of them was tabulated. Consideration was also given to the effect of protecting certain tools to a higher standard than that given above and also to the effect of weighting the loss of production, that is allowing for the condition when the value of the loss became greater than merely the number lost times the value of one unit. Finally a study was made of the reduction of the probable damage that would result from the regrouping of tools, without the addition of structural precautions. After an introductory paragraph FC 23A, the Summary continues:

"A striking fact, made clear by the survey, is the heavy loss of output resulting from damage to certain tools having a high value and a long replacement period. It is clear that the most efficient measures in these factories would be the protection, by means of three-sided pens, of these most vital tools and that, in general, straight runs of protective walling would not be an efficient measure. Structural collapse due to the destruction of a stanchion was also found to be responsible for fairly big losses of output and the elimination of this danger would often be correct.

One lucky bomb dropped on a factory in such a position that it damages a vital machine may seriously reduce output for many months. The cost of building a pen around the machine to protect it from damage by this bomb would be insignificant compared with the value of the lost output. The justification for building the protective pen cannot, however, be decided simply by comparing its cost with the value of the output saved since the probability of that particular bomb dropping must be taken into account.

The economic argument is set out in some detail in the full reports; it is not easily summarised. It may be said, however, that in the case of the SU factory, by scientifically designed protection the area of the factory within which a bomb falling would cause heavy loss, 126 days' output, can be reduced by 3900 square feet at a cost of £2318. In the case of Hobson's factory the figures are 5950 square feet for 175 days' output at a cost of £1467.

The probable saving during the course of the war is this possible saving multiplied by the chance of its being called into play. For example, if the SU factory were situated in an area where the expected future weight of attack was 1 bomb per 100 000 square feet, then the probable saving would be 3900/100 000 × 126 = 4.9 days' output. It is clear that if the value of this probable saving exceeds the cost of the protective measures then the latter are economically justified. In this connection "value" of saving and "cost" of protection may be measured in any convenient units. The comparison is made here in terms of money values, but if the relative scarcity of building and engineering labour were known, then the comparison could easily be made on a man-hour basis.

The concept of probable saving described above provides an excellent measure by which the merits of any protective scheme may be judged. Assuming that the SU figures apply to all light machine shops, then two or three examples will show the application.

(1) Consider a factory situated about 5 miles from the centre of Birmingham, the expected bomb density on the factory being one bomb per 5 000 000 square feet. Suppose that the factory is a bottleneck in the production of aircraft, so that the value of a complete aircraft hangs on each unit produced by the factory. If production is 100 units

a day, then the probable saving that can be achieved by protection is 3900/5 000 000 × 126 × 100 = 9.8 units, the value of which may be 9.8 × £10 000 or £98 000. Since the protection to ensure this saving costs only £2318, it is clearly amply justified. If, on the other hand, the unit manufactured does not constitute a bottleneck but only has its own value of, say £50, then the value of the probable saving is only £490, which at a cost of £2318 is obviously unjustifiable.

(2) Suppose that the factory considered above were either situated at the centre of a very large town, or was of sufficient importance to be a specific object of attack. The expected bomb density on it might then be one bomb per 100 000 square feet. Giving the unit of output only its own value of £50 the probable saving would be 3900/100 000 × 126 × 100 = 490 units worth £24 500 so that here again the protection would be amply justified.

It will be realised that these results are dependent on the value of the expected bomb density. Table 11.1 is included to show some observed values.

TABLE 11.1
Observed intensities of raiding

City	Period* covered by the observations	Observed intensities (sq. ft. per bomb) at distance from the target centre† of–		
		0–2 miles	2–4 miles	4–6 miles
London	13½ months	78 500	153 000	250 000
Birmingham	7⅜ months	222 000	768 000	4 700 000
Hull	9 months	406 000	3 270 000	–

From a random selection of 30 aircraft factories, 15 have been attacked, the average bomb density on these being 1 bomb per 68 000 sq. ft.

Notes: * These are in all cases periods of heavy raiding.
       † The target centre has been taken as the centre of the recorded bombing.

One of the most important points shown by the surveys is the value of redistribution or regrouping of the machines inside the factory. A very substantial insurance from loss of output can be obtained by:
(1) Separating the key machines so that only one is exposed to any one bomb;
(2) grouping round each key machine the other important machines until the limit is reached at which the collective value to output of each type is equal to the value of the key machine.

It was found in the case of the SU factory that limited regrouping, which should not interfere with production, was more effective in reducing the probable loss of output than the structural precautions, already referred to, which would have cost £2318.

It appears from the surveys that all bottleneck factories and all factories in highly vulnerable areas should be protected by regrouping and by structural precautions, the order of priority being: first, bottleneck factories in vulnerable areas; second, bottleneck factories in less vulnerable areas and third, other factories in vulnerable areas. No structural precautions should in general be provided for non-bottleneck factories situated in relatively safe areas and not of sufficient size to be likely objects of specific attack, but in all cases regrouping should be carried out where it does not interfere with production.

It must be stressed, however, that the protective measures to be provided in these factories must be scientifically designed. The construction of long lengths of protective walling in positions chosen by works engineers without a full knowledge of the problem is almost certain to be inefficient. How far the efficiency of such random walls may fall short is shown in Table 11.2. Here the cost and effectiveness of the protection at Hobson's, recommended as a result of the survey is compared with the protection existing at Hobson's and with the protection which might have been recommended by Research and Experiments Department before the principles of protection had been established by the surveys. The efficiencies are in the ratios 59:1:3.''

TABLE 11.2

Comparison of Four Protective Schemes

Measure	Cost (C)	Potential saving (S)	"Equivalent area"* (A) over which this saving applies (sq. ft.)	Efficiency factor $\dfrac{SA}{C}$
Protection recommended for Hobson's Carburettors as a result of the survey	£1467	175 days' output	5950	710
Existing protection at Hobson's Carburettors	£1310	175 days' output	92	12
Protection which would have been recommended for Hobson's prior to the survey	£2280	158 days' output	490	34
Protection recommended for SU Carburettors as a result of the survey	£2318	126 days' output	3900	212

* The "equivalent area" is the area within which the bomb must fall to achieve the potential saving given in Col. 3; it is the area which is made virtually "bombproof" by the protective measures.

Both documents (FC 23 and FC 23A) were circulated to members of the Factory (PAD) Committee for their sixth meeting on 2nd June, 1942. They arrived just in time. Before they were discussed, the Chairman reported that since the last meeting on April 14th concentration of constructional effort on capital contracts had involved radical changes in the control of building labour and works. He invited discussion on the influence which these changes might exert on the execution of works for the protection of production. There is no record of the discussion but it is obvious that the feeling was that structural protection was threatened. However, the impact of the carburettor survey was considerable since the Committee agreed that the Secretary should produce a draft Memorandum for consideration at an extraordinary meeting three days later. This was done and on Saturday 6th June, the day following that meeting, the Committee met again for its seventh formal meeting and confirmed the Memorandum addressed to the Building Directorate. The Chairman, Mr. T. H. Sheepshanks, the new Deputy Secretary, Ministry of Home Security, who had succeeded Sir Harold Scott on April 15th, undertook to forward it to the proper quarter.

The Memorandum set out the main heads under which PAD measures affected the availability of labour for transfer to urgent constructional work, but drew attention to the fact that these could not be dismissed as purely passive and of no importance in connection with offensive operations. It pointed out that, just as the Royal Air Force was doing work of vital importance in destroying enemy aircraft and tanks in their factories before they reached the German field armies, so it was equally important for us to do all we could to preserve the means of producing our own offensive weapons. It mentioned that the average cost of the measures was less than 3% of the building cost of a new factory.

As far as the protection of vital plant was concerned, the Memorandum mentioned the results of the carburettor survey and ends with the recommendation that "Planned protection should be provided for plant in all bottleneck factories and in all vital factories in highly vulnerable areas, e.g. exposed coastal areas, since the survey showed that no alternative use of building labour and materials would maintain output so well, provided that bombing density continued to follow the patterns so far experienced".

No reply from the Building Directorate is recorded but it is clear from the Minutes of the later meetings of the Factory (PAD) Committee that this authority was convinced so that the struggle for the protection of production was won. Moreover it was recognised that the Research and Experiments Departments of the Ministry of Home Security was the proper authority to design this protection.

It will be clear from the last two chapters that the Design and Development Section had been tireless, even aggressive, in their efforts to pass their expert knowledge to the supply Ministries. From early in 1942 courses had been held at Princes Risborough, the Head-quarters of the Research and Experiments Department, for inspectors from other Ministries so that they could receive first hand instruction on how to protect production. Sixteen Ministry of Supply officers had already attended the course before the end of February 1942 and four Admiralty inspectors attended from 23rd to 28th March. The Department had also circulated a document, RE Note 172, setting out the principles in simplified form. The Factory (PAD) Committee, or rather its Standing Sub-committee, at a meeting on 19th November, 1942 recognised that Note 172 was a valuable document but considered that there was a risk of planning being done "inexpertly by enthusiasts". For security reasons it would be inadvisable for Note 172 to be circulated indiscriminately.

It is strange to think of Note 172 being considered a security risk. It was known affectionately at Princes Risborough as the "Kindergarten guide"; it set out simply but soundly the philosophy of protection as derived largely from the carburettor surveys. It gave clear instructions how to plan redistribution or regrouping of machines but pointed out that this would only improve the chance of survival of output. Where plant and products were valuable in themselves structural protection was essential. For this, elegant graphical methods were described enabling the non-mathematical to choose the correct height of protective wall, to plan the shape of pen to surround an individual machine or a group of machines, similar or dissimilar, and to decide when a pen should be roofed.

The Standing Sub-committee suggested that a brief article should appear in "ARP Industrial Bulletins" drawing attention to the need for foresight on planning factories and giving notice that at the outset of a new enterprise expert advice should be obtained from the Research and Experiments Department, so my own little struggle was won just three years after I had first started it.

There were occasional signs of rebellion; for instance at the ninth meeting of the main Committee on 2nd October, 1942 the Ministry of Supply representative asked if the Committee had agreed that protective walls were not to be built indiscriminately but only in those factories where they could be employed to special advantage. The Ministry of Aircraft Production representative sprang to our defence, saying he understood that the Committee had agreed that half measures were not worthwhile; a factory should be considered as a whole and any cases worthy of treatment should be referred to Research and Experiments Department and the protection should be planned in collaboration with that Department.

Again at the tenth meeting on 18th December, 1942 the Admiralty was detected in the shocking crime of publishing, for the use of its own inspectors, a circular on the strengthening on the roof structures of factories. The Ministry of Home Security representative said there was no objection to the circular on technical grounds but the accepted view was that no structural strengthening should be contemplated unless the factory was one where the need for the protection of production was generally agreed. In such cases the Ministry of Supply and Ministry of Aircraft Production did, in fact, consult Research and Experiments and since this seemed to work well there was no need for the Admiralty to alter the arrangement.

However, no sooner was the case for protection accepted and an orderly system developed than the brake had to be applied. The economic justification for protecting production depended on the intensity of bombing. Though a series of heavy raids on London was to start again on 21st January, 1944 and to last until the end of March, with sharp attacks also on Hull, Bristol and South Wales, the intensity of bombing had fallen appreciably by the spring of 1943 so that as early as 16th April of that year the Ministry of Aircraft Production was justified in drawing up a Memorandum for the Factory (PAD) Committee the first paragraph of which read:

"The development of the war situation, the growing shortage of building labour and materials and the demands for offensive purposes on the limited resources that are available make it essential to restrict to the maximum extent possible the expenditure of labour and materials on defensive measures." The Memorandum dealt in the main with the need to relax the provision of the Act of 1939.

As a result a new Defence Regulation was made introducing certain modifications to the Civil Defence Act 1939. The effect of the Regulation in relation to factory premises was explained in a Memorandum by the Ministry of Home Security dated 8th June, 1943. The clause relating to the protection of production was amended to read:

"(7) Measures for the protection of vital plant should be limited to cases in the highest category of vital list factories or where there are risks of a special character."

The last business of the Factory (PAD) Committee at its twelfth meeting on 15th June, 1943 was to consider amendments to this Ministry of Home Security Memorandum. No amendment was proposed to Clause 7.

So ended one short-lived, hectic but entertaining, branch of production engineering.

CHAPTER 12

Postscript

In the summer of 1943 I received a surprising invitation—almost a command—to apply for the Chair of Mechanical Sciences at Cambridge University which was about to become vacant. Cambridge had not been entirely emptied of staff and students in the Second War as it had been in the First because of the national policy of directing scientific personnel into positions of the greatest benefit to the war effort. The education and training of engineers was continued so that the Cambridge Engineering Department instead of being reduced to a handful of students, as in the 1914–18 War, was bursting at the seams. Not only were the usual degree courses going full blast but the Department, in its enthusiasm, had undertaken to provide short elementary courses for young officers of all the fighting services. The Head of the Department, Professor Charles Inglis, had reached the retiring age in September 1940 but had generously agreed, at the request of the University authorities, to stay on for another three years. Towards the end of that period the University proceeded to the election of a successor.

Though I knew how well off we had been in Bristol and was looking forward to returning there as soon as the War would allow, sentiments strongly echoed by my wife, I was ingenuous enough at that time to feel that if Cambridge needed me then, as a Cambridge man, I must obey the call. I shared with a good many others the opinion that the Cambridge Department, of which I would be in charge, was the greatest teaching institution in the world and was potentially of importance scientifically. At least it was large, constituting one tenth of the whole University of Cambridge, so it presented a challenge. The invitation came at an opportune moment. My main work in Civil Defence was virtually completed. As described in the last chapter, the protection of production had been put on to a rational basis before the weight of enemy attack fell below the level at which protection was justified, and though attacks on the country by flying bombs and V2 rockets were expected it was considered that the air raid shelters already designed, as described in Chapters 5 and 6, would be adequate (orders were placed in September 1943 for an additional 100 000 Morrison shelters). I also had a feeling, which will be readily understood by the reader of this book, that the Ministry of Home Security and others would not be sorry to see me go. In August 1943, therefore, while retaining my membership of the Civil Defence Research Committee and many other wartime bodies, I resigned from my full-time post as Scientific Adviser and from the Bristol Chair, accepted the Professorship of Mechanical Sciences and moved to Cambridge. There for 25 years I was fully occupied with the work of my University department, as described briefly by Norman Hilken in his history.[1]

In October 1946 Bill Tyhurst, our Bristol friend, drew my attention to the fact that a Royal Commission on Awards to Inventors had been set up in May of that year. After a

[1] T. J. N. Hilken, *Engineering at Cambridge University 1783–1965*, CUP, 1967.

great deal of thought I decided to make a claim based on the clear cut case of the invention of the Morrison shelter for which a patent, Specification No. 548069 "Improvements in and relating to Air Raid Shelters", had been taken out in my name by the Ministry of Home Security in 1940 as a protective measure against wild claimants.

Simple vanity must have played a part but my decision was largely influenced by the need to stress the importance of the engineer in successful innovation (at that time all the emphasis was on the importance of the "scientist"), and the feeling, justified by later events, that the new principle of absorbing energy by plastic deformation would be ignored by British industry if it did not receive publicity. There was also the realisation, after three years' experience, that being Head of the Engineering Department was very much a full time job leaving no time, energy or interest for consulting work, so that any financial reward for past services would be useful.

The first rule of procedure set down by the Royal Commission stated.

"The claimant shall, in the first instance, submit his claim in writing to the Government department whose use of the invention, design drawing or process, has given rise to the claim."

So on 23rd November, 1946 I wrote to the Assistant Under-secretary, Civil Defence (Home Office).

"I beg to submit a claim for an award for the invention and design of the table (Morrison) indoor shelter issued to the public during the war by the Ministry of Home Security.

"A copy of the relevant patent specification No. 548069 'Improvements in and relating to Air Raid Shelters' is enclosed."

Then followed a protracted and very pretty example of Civil Service "off-putting", which lasted for the better part of four years. It can best be illustrated in the form of the diary of events later enclosed as an exhibit for the Commission.

23rd November 1946
  Wrote to Home Office lodging my Claim.
26th January 1947
  Wrote reminding Home Office of letter of 23rd November 1946, which had not been acknowledged.
29th March 1947
  Wrote a personal letter to Sir John Hodsoll, Inspector General (Civil Defence) Home Office, asking for his help.
2nd April 1947
  Offer from Hodsoll of help in reminding Home Office of my earlier letters.
10th April 1947
  Apologies and official acknowledgment from Home Office of letters of 23rd November 1946 and 26th January 1947 "Which had been overlooked".
25th September 1947
  Again wrote to Home Office reminding them of my Claim.
16th November 1947
  Telephoned Home Office and was told that Claim had been referred to Ministry of Supply.
17th November 1947
  Wrote to Patents Claims Officer, Ministry of Supply, mentioning that the Home

Office had referred the matter of my claim to the Ministry of Supply and asking when a decision could be expected.

2nd December 1947

Reply from Ministry of Supply saying that no trace could be found of earlier Claim addressed to the Home Office but in view of my letter to the Ministry of Supply, consideration of my Claim would be initiated.

6th December 1947

Sent Ministry of Supply copies of correspondence with Home Office as requested.

8th December 1947

Wrote to Home Office asking them to pass relevant information to Ministry of Supply.

11th December 1947

Acknowledgment of letter of 6th December from Ministry of Supply.

31st December 1947

Apologetic letter from Home Office saying,

"I am sorry that consideration of your application for an Award in respect of the design of the Morrison shelter has been so long delayed. The matter has, however, been the subject of discussion with the principal Patents and Awards Officer, who has requested to be furnished with certain information. This is now being assembled and will be communicated to him with as little further delay as possible."

18th June 1948

Sent to Ministry of Supply, as a reminder, the proof of a paper dealing with the design of the Morrison shelter which was about to be published by the Institution of Civil Engineers.

30th June 1948

Acknowledgment from Ministry of Supply also stating that due to urgent work on cases before the Royal Commission the investigations regarding the Claim had not yet been completed. A further communication would be sent as soon as possible.

23rd March 1949

Letter signed by A. J. Edmunds from Home Office saying that Claim had been considered by the Inventions Awards Committee of Ministry of Supply, a Committee specially constituted to deal with Claims by Crown Servants, which did not feel able to recommend an award.

29th April 1949

Wrote to Ministry of Supply asking for guidance as follows, "On my return last week from a visit to the United States I found a letter dated 23rd March, 1949 from the Civil Defence Department, Home Office, informing me that the Inventions Awards Committee did not feel able to make me an award. Could you tell me what steps I have now to take as I presume this is not a final decision of the Royal Commission. It would have been surprising indeed if the Department which did its best to resist in 1940 the adoption of the shelter I designed had recommended an award to me now."

15th July 1949

Wrote to Edmunds at the Home Office.

"I have to thank you for your letter of 23rd March, 1949 informing me that you are unable to recommend an award for the design of the indoor table shelter distributed by the Ministry of Home Security during the War. I am sorry to have delayed so long in replying to your letter but I was in the United States on business at that time and have not had the opportunity of dealing with private correspondence since my return.

I am naturally disappointed to hear your decision. It appears from the rules of procedure, Royal Commission on Awards to Inventors, that the next step is to notify the Secretary of the Commission that it has not been possible to reach a settlement. I hope that the Home Office will do this without delay as my original Claim, having been made on 23rd November, 1946, it took you nearly $2\frac{1}{2}$ years to come to the decision contained in your letter of 23rd March, 1949.

I am going abroad again on the 6th August for a few weeks but I hope that you will be able to let me know before that date that the Home Office is willing for the Claim to be referred to the Commission."

19th July 1949

Letter from Edmunds as follows,

"Thank you for your letter dated 15th July. I had not forgotten our telephone conversations but shortly after I last spoke to you I received from the Ministry of Supply a copy of the letter you sent them on the 29th April in which you made, for the first time, so far as I am aware, what is to me the wholly surprising and unexpected suggestion that the Ministry of Home Security "did its best to resist in 1940 the adoption of the shelter" which forms the subject of your Claim. It will be necessary to go carefully into this point before we decide upon our future course of action and I should, therefore, be glad if you would be kind enough to let me have in as much detail as possible a statement on the grounds on which you base the allegation in your letter of the 29th April."

24th July 1949

Wrote to Edmunds giving him a short statement about circumstances leading up to design and adoption of shelter (as recorded in Chapter 6) and ending,

"If Sir Alexander Rouse is still with you he will, I feel sure, be able to bear out this account and to supply you with any more details you may require."

4th October 1949

Wrote and telephoned to Home Office at frequent intervals until a letter dated 4th October arrived from Edmunds saying "I seem doomed to have to apologise to you but I have only just been able to crawl back to duty after a longish bout of sick leave. I shall be happy to have a talk with you when you are next in town and perhaps you would be kind enough to give me a day or two's notice of the day and time which would be most convenient to you."

21st October 1949

Interview at Home Office at which I was told that as I was a temporary Civil Servant during the war I could not take my Claim to the Royal Commission without the permission of the Home Office. I was led to understand this was not likely to be given. Recounted in more detail how the Morrison came to be designed and urged the Home Office to reconsider their decision.

5th November 1949

Letter from Edmunds at the Home Office to say that the Royal Commission was being asked to enquire into the circumstances of my Claim and that the Commission would get in touch with me direct.

4th May 1950

Having heard nothing from the Commission I wrote asking when I could expect my Claim to be heard.

8th May 1950

Letter from Secretary, Royal Commission, saying my Claim had not been referred to the Commission and until this happened the Commission could not deal with it. Nevertheless he had written to the Home Office about it.

6th June 1950

Letter from Secretary, Royal Commission, stating that they had now been requested under Head 3 of the terms of reference to enquire into the circumstances of the Claim and enclosing the necessary forms to be completed and other information.

18th December 1950

Hearing of Claim before Royal Commission.

After the Royal Commission machinery went into operation on 6th June the whole tone, tenor and tempo of the business changed. The staff of the Commission, particularly the Secretary, R. G. Lloyd,[2] and S. W. Slaughter of the Ministry of Supply, whose business it was to prepare the brief for the Home Office, were unsparing in their help. They saw me and gave invaluable advice and guidance time after time, patiently and quite outside the bounds of normal duty. Though the shortened procedure was to be followed and I was to conduct my own case, an immense amount of work had to be accomplished in the six months. Searches of files and hunts for evidence were made for both sides. Seven "bundles" containing all the evidence and relevant documents had to be prepared for the members of the Commission. D. C. Burn was the helpful member of the old RE4 Design and Development Section. He, together with Sir Alexander Rouse and Leader-Williams, were to be called as witnesses by the Home Office. Sir Reginald Stradling, formerly in charge of the Research and Experiments Department refused to give evidence. In a letter of 30th October, 1950 he said:

"My reasons are two—(a) my memory of the detail are too vague and I have no records to which I can refer, and (b) I feel that my evidence might go against you—certainly I do not think I could stand up to serious cross-examination.

"As I see it the problem is whether you, and *you alone*, were responsible for the idea of the Morrison shelter. You used to argue with me about names of your staff being attached to papers, etc., and emphasised how much you were trying to work your group as an integrated team. This is my difficulty, I honestly do not know the extent to which you were personally responsible."

Many others found their memories unreliable. A delightful exception was F. Webster, one time deputy Chief Engineer, who, in a helpful letter of 8th November, recollected that it was he who passed on the tip to make a prototype shelter to take to Downing Street.

Long before the case came up for hearing I was heartily sick of the whole venture. It had been something of a shock that the Ministry was opposing the claim so vigorously and it was no pleasure to have those who had been such close colleagues, particularly Leader-Williams, arrayed against me. However, I had only myself to blame for setting the machine in motion and it was likely to be a fitting postscript to my somewhat turbulent career as a temporary Civil Servant.

The purpose of the shortened procedure was to provide a simple and expeditious way of

---

[2] Now Lord Lloyd of Kilgerran, CBE., QC.

bringing Claims to a hearing in those cases in which the relevant facts and the matters in issue were susceptible of concise statement. A form was provided which had to be completed by the Claimant, the statements were to provide a summary of the material facts upon which the Claim was based. The evidence by which these facts were to be proved at the hearing were not to be given on the form.

Upon receipt of the form the Secretary was to obtain the comments of the Government Department concerned and a copy of these comments was to be supplied to the Claimant. The Commission hoped that the shortened procedure would, in most cases, enable a Claimant to present his case in person and this I decided to do. Apart from the expense I was averse to briefing Counsel because this seemed too professional and cold-blooded a way of going about the matter. To my surprise the shortened procedure did not prevent the other side from employing a highly skilled professional advocate to conduct their case.

The questions to be answered on the form were (1) Name and address of Claimant, (2) If the Claimant is or was at any time serving in the Armed Forces or in a Government Department, (3) Description of the invention, design, drawing or process disclosed, (4) Name of department to which disclosure was made, (5) Nature, extent and period of its use by the Government department, (6) Brief particulars of any personal services relied on and rendered by the Claimant to the department in connection with the subject matter of the Claim, and in summary form any other information which the Claimant considers relevant to his Claim.

There is no need to give details of the answers to these questions, they can be deduced from the department's comments which were received on the 20th October, 1950. This document stated:

"(1) The Department admits paragraphs 1–5 inclusive of the Claimant's statement of Claim.

(2) The Department will contend that (a) although the Claimant still held his Chair at the University of Bristol at the material time he was, at that time, a full time paid servant of the Ministry of Security, (b) the Claimant was invited to join the Ministry of Home Security because of his pre-war research work on structures, (c) the Claimant was not the originator of the idea of having an air raid shelter indoors, (d) the Claimant worked on the design of the Morrison shelter as the result of a specific request.

(3) 1 174 201 Morrison shelters were made and issued to the public. Their average cost was £7. 12s. 6d.

(4) The Department will also contend that the design of the Morrison shelter was not produced by the Claimant unaided but was the result of team work on the part of several Crown Servants, at least two of whom made substantial, if not vital, contributions to the design. That the work fell wholly within the scope of the duties of the team who were in a favourable position as a result of the knowledge gained in the course of their duties and of the departmental facilities available to them and that the design is not of such exceptional brilliance as to justify an Award."

Later Slaughter enclosed in a letter dated 9th December a list of questions the Ministry side proposed to put to Leader-Williams and to Burn and another that they were to put to Sir Alexander Rouse. The letter said:

"You will see that at the end of the list of questions to be put to Messrs. Leader-Williams and Burn we have included one about official opposition. I am not sure that you will want us to ask this for purely personal reasons. We have put it down because you refer to official opposition in your Statement of Claim, but I think you said during one of your visits here that you did not want to make much of this. At any rate if you have any real objection to that question being put perhaps you would let us know."

In my reply of 15th December I said:

"Thank you for the questions. With regard to Burn and Leader's No. 11 (would you say that there was any official opposition to the adoption of the Morrison indoor air raid shelter beyond what is commonly met with when something new is advocated?) I have no real objection; I will keep the party as clean as possible but this seems to me quite harmless."

Slaughter in addition to providing all this helpful information with great forethought had arranged for the original prototype shelter shown to Mr. Churchill to be moved from the Imperial War Museum, to which it had been presented after the war, to the Court Room at Somerset House, so that I could set out my papers on it and use it for demonstration. There I found it installed at 11.0 a.m. on 18th December when the case was opened.

Seven members of the Commission under the Chairmanship of Lord Justice Cohen heard the case. I had never been in a court of any kind before and if it had not been for the careful instructions of Lloyd and Slaughter I would not have had any idea how to present my case. My prepared brief was about 10 000 words long covering much of the contents of Chapters 4, 6 and 7, and I kept as closely to this as time would allow. The members of the Commission listened with great patience to all I had to say, including the elementary science of Chapter 4. I struggled through the cross-examination somehow, being guided from time to time by Lord Cohen who would interject the remark "Professor Baker you are cross-examining not giving evidence". As well as stubbornness and persistence there must be a streak of sadism in my make-up because I positively enjoyed cross-examining Sir Alexander Rouse and Leader-Williams. However by the end of the afternoon when the case came to an end I crawled back to my London club as exhausted as if I had spent the whole day playing a non-stop game of Rugby football.

On 20th December, 1950 I wrote to Lloyd:

"I hasten to write before I hear any more of my case, one way or the other, to thank you for the kindness and consideration I received at your hands and from your staff in the dealings of the last few months. Without your help I am certain that my case would not have come before the Royal Commission as quickly as it did and it is encouraging to be reminded that there are Government departments which are well administered.

"I cannot say that I enjoyed Monday but it was an experience. I feel also that I was treated most considerately by the members of the Commission. The only regrets I have are that . . . a sense of urgency crept into the proceedings so that I did not feel it good policy to continue to demolish Leader-Williams' evidence. However, as it also led to me scrapping my wonderful peroration I daresay it was all to the good."

Lloyd replied in a letter dated 29th December:

"It was very kind of you to trouble to write and thank us for the procedural assistance the secretariat had given you and I hope the final result of the award by the Commission is not too displeasing. 'Officialdom' has been shocked at the Commission's munificence!

"It is, of course, the natural reaction of a good advocate to think when it is all over how much better he would have done the case if only he could try again. You certainly did very well in putting the facts of your case across. Really there was little controversy in your Claim because the principal facts stood out so much. You will recall that I warned you on the morning of the hearing that another case was in the list to be opened in the afternoon but that you should disregard that time-table and not limit your evidence. Perhaps it is as well that the peroration was not delivered after all! They can be dangerous things!"

Before Lloyd's letter arrived I had received from the Commission a copy of the Recommendation which it had sent to the Treasury. It read as follows:

"The Commission having enquired under Head 3 of the Royal Warrant into the Claim dated 6th July, 1950 by Professor J. F. Baker, OBE recommend, having regard to all the circumstances, that the sum of £3000 (THREE THOUSAND POUNDS) be paid to him for his design of the air raid shelter known as the Morrison shelter.

Signed Lionel L. Cohen
Chairman"

I was content; I had won my case. I had successfully dealt a blow at bureaucratic obstruction as everyone who values true democracy must do whenever it is found not only in Government departments but in University faculties or public companies. The amount of the Award though not a fortune, even by the standards of 1950, was sufficient measured by the Awards made to other inventors, to show that my work had been considered of importance to the war effort. Where I had failed, and time alone showed this, was to encourage British industry to use in peace-time products the principle of absorbing energy by plastic deformation which had been so valuable in war, though the same basic plastic principles applied to static problems were to revolutionise the design of steel framed buildings and to be used throughout the world.[3]

[3] Baker J. F., Horne, M. R. and Heyman J, *The Steel Skeleton*, Vol. II, CUP, 1956.

Index